54 Steps to Happiness

or

How to lose weight by realising what you want

By Michael Wash

Author of 54 Simple Truths with Brutal Advice

First published in Great Britain by MWA Publications 2008

© Mike Wash

Mike Wash has asserted his right under the Copyright, Designs and Patents Act 1988 to be identified as the author of the book.

A CIP record for this book is available from the British Library.

ISBN 978 0 9536448 2 7

Typeset, printed and bound in Great Britain by
York Publishing Services Ltd
64 Hallfield Road
Layerthorpe
York YO31 7ZQ
Tel: 01904 431213   Website: www.yps-publishing.co.uk

Introduction

Despite my best efforts to accept the way I am and to lose weight, at best, I yo-yo diet and always put the weight back on. At worse – over the years, I have got bigger every year. I started writing this journal as a way of challenging myself to be honest with what I am thinking and doing. My suspicions about the link between healthy mind, healthy body = happiness is explored throughout this journal.

On a daily basis for 6 months, I recorded my personal thoughts. This process took me to some weird and sometimes tragic places, all of which – at some time – have been part of my life.

It became apparent that to lose weight permanently, the change had to be part of who I really was. So this is more than a book about losing weight – it's a journal recording the rediscovery of myself, and the realisation of what I really want.

It touches on grief, cancer, depression, delusions, divorce, suicide, family, love, parenthood, distorted beliefs, hopes, dreams and wonderful experiences and celebration of life.

This 6 months is a snapshot in history as I found it difficult to ignore world events. A world at war and one that was still recovering from a tsunami and terrorist attacks in the USA, UK, Iraq, Afghanistan, Delhi and Jordan. Also, earthquakes and hurricanes, riots on the streets about religion, race and rights to work.

It's been an amazing 6 months which I hope have set me on the journey of health and happiness. I open up my story to you with a hope that it may stir perhaps at least one insight into your own story that contributes to your own health and happiness.

Mike Wash

Contents

Dedication

To you who seek peace in body, mind and spirit and strive to find courage to lead a long and healthy life.

Acknowledgements

To Mave, my wife; Philippa, my stepdaughter and Caren, my PA and Office Manager – all of whom are an inspiration to me.

To my sons; Thomas and Matthew, who are also great friends and fun to be with.

To my stepson; Myles – the most helpful man I know!

To my sisters, whose love and support I will always cherish.

1. The Full Fat Version

The Diary – The Full Fat Version

23.09.2005   Day 1

That's it! Enough is enough! Years and years of trying to lose weight. Who's kidding who, diets don't work, the only solution – surgery! Just kidding, although sometimes wonder if it would be easier to slice off that blob of lard protruding over my belt. I think I will give it a name – it has had a lot of attention over the years, spoilt, over indulged, heaving oval shape supported by significant 'love handles' either side – let's call it 'Blobby' – no too obvious – the Hulk – no – that's insulting to the green giant character – I know 'Fatmea' [a play on 'a fat me'] – yes, Fatmea must go!

So, you want to know how much I weigh. Well, for my height – a smidging over 6 ft – I should be around 13 ½ stone (according to those wonderful weight tables). Anyway, that means at 17 ½ stone – 245 lbs – I am obese. OBESE! 4 stone overweight – I haven't been 13 ½ stone for 20 years – then I was running half marathons – indeed completed the London marathon in 1985 in under 4 hours! (I was 13 stone then). (OK only a few seconds under – but still respectable!).

If I try running now not only will my knees give way but the Council won't be too pleased with the damage I cause to the pavement!

So, I am classed as obese – Yikes! It sounds like a disease – well I suppose it is, particularly at my age (51 next week!). It means I am at risk of high blood pressure, stroke, heart attack, cancer (already had that one – more of that later) and problems with my joints – not to mention diabetes with its association with blindness! Scared yet?

Nah – not me – I've known this for years. I'm the guy who had chest pains one evening so decided to go for a run to see if it was anything more than indigestion – crazy huh?

OK, let's hear the case for Fatmea, she is pleasure (is she a she? Yes, I think so – something to do with if she wasn't there I would be more masculine and look less like a pregnant duck!") She is comfort, relaxed in social company, relates to being big, big is strong, protective and warm. It's good to have a big appetite, to finish everything on your plate, appreciate food, think you're lucky you're not in the Third World and starving and well, er, hum, maybe – OK now I'm struggling. I did win the bonniest baby competition at Butlins Holiday Camp in 1955 and I was a big chubby baby, and I did come third in a Tarzan competition in 1966 again at Butlins – so you see – not all bad. Oh and I was a pretty good rugby player at 18 weighing in at 16 stone then! So, rewarded well for size! Fatmea stay? No, I have decided – she has got to go.

By the way, I have found this new level of commitment and insight at the worst possible time. I am writing this on the plane all set for a two week holiday in Florida. Fatmea is in good company over there – amongst the extremely obese and the triple XXX obese and the close to death obese so making Fatmea look small which is a great incentive for adding another half stone! Also – Christmas is not too far away and we all know what happens then – the odds are against us, chances are slim – I mean fat!

Great start to the day – set off on time – a few minor motorway delays then – urgent news, terrorist alert, Manchester Airport closed – passengers advised not to come to the airport. Great – apparently some crazy idiot managed to get onto the runway with a suitcase – he was zapped by a stun gun, bomb squad called in and now everyone is delayed at least 3 hours! This called for a pint of beer and a sandwich especially since I had no breakfast! It could have been worse – could have been 2 pints and packet of crisps. I must not give myself a bad time over this – it's not what you eat it's how much. If you put in more than you use – you gain weight. A simple truth. So, eat less and exercise more – that's all there is to it!

We are going on holiday all three of us. Fatmea, my wife and me. My wife, Mave, my gorgeous loving wife – who has just said I have to lose weight to be healthy so I can live longer so we can be together long. She's the best thing that has ever happened to me and not only do I want to live longer for us, but for my own children who are generating their family – so I have a beautiful grandson – Oliver – and one of my ambitions is to take my Grandchildren to Disney – so I need to keep well and healthy – it's down to me – so come on Michael – wake up and smell the coffee – get real – you can do it!

THOUGHT FOR THE DAY
First Step – accept and understand you have a problem and only you can solve it!

24.09.2005   Day 2

Well we arrived in Florida – sunshine state for the fatties! I will be in good company. An aspect of living out here is that you wear very few clothes – shorts and a tank top for me and often wandering around with only my swimming trunks on. I can't avoid those mirrors or reflections in the glass – OK – so have a closer look – look at the over-hanging wobbly flesh. Yuk! Look at those breasts growing, and your face getting rounder and that chin wobbling – OK enough of the horror movie!

Curious thing body image – I can spend a lot of time denying being overweight and looking good, wearing loose clothing, large suits, black is a good colour – but take it all off and have a good honest look – not a pretty sight.

So improving health is one motivator, looking good and feeling good about yourself is another. Feeling attractive – mmm? – well? I am fortunate to have a wife who thinks I am attractive and loves her 'hulk', her big man – that's good, but ideally I also need to feel I am attractive and not repulsive. Getting on in years too is confronting to one's own body image – seeing the grey hairs (what's left of my hair), getting the next prescription for glasses tells me – this body is increasingly going to need looking after.

This miracle of a body, every cell connects, every cell dies and new ones are created every day, its automatic functions are amazing, but the most amazing thing for me – is our own sense of self. I believe I can change my thoughts, my emotions and my behaviour just by raising my level of awareness of who I am and what am I doing in every moment. So do it stupid! I do from time to time – mornings are best, quiet time, exercise, then the day gets busier and by the time we are into the evening – it's a few beers and snacks, TV on and hi – 'me' the 'I' is somewhere else – so let's have another drink and a few more snacks – get the picture? I have to somehow bring my awareness of what I am doing into the times I am most vulnerable to the temptations of drinking, overeating, snacking and slouching.

I have realised over the years, and from trying every diet around, from Atkins to Slimming World, Weight Watchers and even cabbage soup, that diets don't work! Yes, of course you lose some weight after a short while, but it all goes on again unless a fundamental change of habits and / or behaviour occurs, ie eat less, exercise more. It's not what you eat, it's how much. You can lose weight just eating fish and chips and Indian curries as long as the equation energy in is less than energy out. No matter what diet you take up, unless this equation is involved – you won't lose weight. Diets work partly by raising your awareness of what you are eating and the consequences – well I believe this fundamental point – awareness and consciousness. Having the ability to stand back and look at yourself and be in charge – in my case stopping 'Fatmea' dominating my life! Fatmea will sometimes think about what to eat next before she's finished what she is currently eating! Fatmea will eat whilst watching TV and hardly remember eating or what it tastes like! So, Fatmea, you have to be put in your place, preferably not around my midriff – which, by the way – being apple shaped and having excess abdominal fat, doubles the chance of a heart attack!

OK, a bit of housework, DIY and then golf. Now golf is an incredible mirror to life – I mean how you play it – golfers will understand this – non golfers will frown – I'll explain later when the moment's right.

By the way – no fancy recipes or secret short cuts here – just try and eat a little less each day and be conscious, aware – make it a real choice as to what you are putting in your mouth to feed Fatmea (the Temptress!).

THOUGHT FOR THE DAY
When you put food in your mouth – ask yourself why?

25.09.05   Day 3

Now, I am going to sound a bit crazy for a while – so be prepared. When I was 30 I was diagnosed with Testicular cancer – now that brought tears to my eyes! However, apparently there are two types – one aggressive the other a wimp! I got the wimp – lucky huh! Well, having cancer and going through radiotherapy ain't a lot of fun but what it gives you is a realisation every day of what you have got. A real appreciation of life and how precious it is. Just spend a moment outside, find a quiet place and listen, smell, see, feel, touch – now those are the real wonders and miracles of the world. I thought there were seven wonders of the world – there are – the other two? To give and forgive (more of that later!)

Back to my cancer – what it also left me with is a real fear of dying younger with cancer and a picture of myself all wasted, thin, emaciated and dying. So – one way of combating the reality of this picture in my head is to be big and strong – so I can't have cancer whilst I am big! (See, I told you it was crazy!). What this is really about is facing up to one's fears. Fears of dying, losing a loved one, fear of rejection, fear of failure. It's all in one shape or another fear of loss. The thing to remember here is that the fear itself can stop you experiencing what you have now, so in effect your fear is contributing to the loss – makes sense? Doesn't matter if it doesn't – just don't be frightened of facing your own vulnerability. Men in particular like to convey this strong, 'I'm OK' image – and deny to themselves that inside is a small child, a scared young man or a lonely old man – it's OK – I am all these things, but you know at the end of the day – all I have got is me, my health and my ability to experience the miracles and wonders of life – without that – there is nothing. So I am not going to waste my time being anxious, stressed or frightened – all this does is to stop you experiencing the moment. Fatmea doesn't need food, she needs love, joy, fun and happiness – this is the most effective diet of all – the diet of life.

THOUGHT FOR THE DAY
Eat less, drink less, fear less, be more.

26.09.05   Day 4

OK, so how's the 'feed fest' going? Well, cereal, orange juice for breakfast, ham and cheese sandwich for lunch and for dinner 2½ pints of beer, ¾ bottle of wine and a couple of Italian Starters, which included fried calamari and mozzarella cheese - oh and a large bag of crisps! Good diet huh? Now, before you condemn Fatmea and me - the difference today from most other days is - that each mouthful (well most) I was aware and I ate less yesterday than the previous day. Combine this with my 20 minute aerobic bike exercise and a game of golf - I think E out > E in (energy out was greater than energy in) so a few fat globules will have been used up!

Small steps in the right direction is better than a leap in the dark - this has to be a long journey - rest of my life - so it has to be fundamental. It needs to go deep and affect my view of the world, people and food - or the need for food. Why do I eat when I am not hungry? What is it satisfying? Are your ready for some psychobabble? Here goes....

Putting things in my mouth - reminds me of a time when I was warm, secure and loved, ie: in my mothers' arms feeding from her breast. So, deep down I am compensating for not having my mothers' love. This may not be too far fetched as my mother died tragically nearly 30 years ago - I was only a young man and never really got to know my mum as an adult, nor did she get to know my children. She was in an accident, fell off a balcony in Singapore and was in a coma for three, or was it four, years before she died. My dominant images of her are in the coma - I have very few images of her before then - so this trauma and grief could be playing a part in my life today. I wish I had spoken to her more and cuddled her more when she was in the coma - I am sure she was aware at some level of her loved ones around her.

Regret and grief and past traumas do have an emotional pull today - and it can keep you 'stuck' if you let it. Now, this isn't the cause of 'Fatmea' being dominant (I was a big man before my mothers' death) but it may be a contributing factor to why I am still overweight! Now, you think that's tragic - wait until I tell you about my sister! Anyway - the point here is again - face up to what happened - recognise the pain and trauma - then move on, let it go! Seeking pleasure and comfort in food will not make the pain go away or compensate for the love of my mother in anyway. It's in the past – and if you think about it – the past doesn't exist, it's gone, all it is is thoughts and feelings about those thoughts in your head. If you live in the past and let these thoughts and feelings dominate, you will not move on, and – more importantly, you will miss out on what's happening now, this very moment!

THOUGHT FOR THE DAY
If your mum is still alive – cherish her, oh, and let go of the past, live for the moment.

27.09.2005   Day 5

Every time we come to Florida, we do little improvements around our Villa. Yes, our Villa! This has been an ambition of mine for years, and with Mave's support and hard work we have managed to own a villa near Disney now for the past eight years. We hire it out so we can just about afford to keep it. Anyway – my job – the front garden. Cutting away at the palm tree – I got stung by some big black flying thing – it stung me through a glove, I can see the hole it made, and boy – has my hand swollen up!!! Anyway – didn't stop me playing golf later and did my best ever back 9 – gross 41!

Had a steak, salad and coconut shrimp with the usual beer, wine and snacks. I think last year I would have eaten even more, but I am, believe it or not, restricting myself – but not to the extent of depriving me of a good time. Fatmea has been with me all my life, so a slow farewell is probably healthier and longer lasting.

This is my last day of being 50! I didn't celebrate being 50 – I think I was quite depressed – it followed two bad business years where essentially, I was unemployed (although I work for myself) which led us into selling a nice big house and buying a smaller one and paying off our debts so the pressure to earn is reduced. So, celebrating 50 didn't seem right, but 51 – yes!! If you think about it – when you look at how long you have left to live – after you have taken off a third for sleeping, time for work, time giving to others, travelling, stuck in traffic, being ill or unable to function for whatever reason

– assuming I live to 85, it means out of the 35 years left:

     12 sleep
     5 being ill or incapacitated in some way
     5 time for others
     5 work and other things

this leaves 8 healthy years left for me!

Now, if I don't lose weight – then I am likely to die before 85 – say 80 or 78 then that means I only have a year left for me.

If you were given only a few years to live – what would you do with them? Now, there's a question! From time to time, I ask myself 'would I want to be doing anything different right now?' Lately, the answer is no. I am very happy exactly where I am (apart from this relationship with Fatmea – which is changing). One thing I love about being human is the fact that we have choice – we can choose to change our circumstances or change the way we live with our circumstances. Either way; happiness, peace and fulfilment is within our grasp.

Easier said than done for those living in poverty, war or live under persecution or threat.

My heart goes out to all those living in life threatening circumstances – I get angry with the incompetence of government, the futility of war and laziness of humanity to get of their big fat arse and help those in greater need. We have become so materialistic in this world it's beyond a joke – people forget what's really precious around here – not your house, your car or your fine clothes and jewels – it's your health, your relationships and the love you choose to give and receive.

Oops, went on a bit there didn't I? Soap box stuff – so where was I, ah, yes – making the most of the time you have left and choosing to live it how you want.

THOUGHT FOR THE DAY (LAST DAY OF BEING 50!)
When cutting Palms in Florida – wear thicker gloves – and
– It's not how long you live that's important, it's how you choose to live.

28.09.2005   Day 6 (51!)

Happy birthday to me, happy birthday to me, happy birthday dear me and Fatmea! Happy birthday to me!!

Didn't eat much yesterday but boy did I drink! Drinking = calories too stupid! It also weakens the resolve, increases chance of snacking and drinking one too many too often. Back home it's getting to habit stage – three cans of lager a night – over here it's that plus the wine. What's the point – it only makes me sleepy – I nod off early and wake up with a fuzzy head. So, why don't I stop it or at least moderate it? Let's try – even on my birthday!

Drinking also slowly hardens the liver and erodes the brain cells and increases the onset of memory loss – OK – convinced – that's another step in the right direction.

I find this self talk quite therapeutic really – putting down my thoughts helps me listen to who I am – yes – me – who – Mikey!!

Standing back and observing yourself, listen to your thoughts, check out how you are feeling and ask yourself – is it OK?

If not, then change it! We have phenomenal potential as human beings for joy and love, yet it's amazing how often this is forgotten or masked by our need for power, control and status. Standing back and trying to see the real you – through all the superficial trappings of life is a real challenge.

I am not my status, I am my presence
I am not my income, I am valuable
I am not my material world, I am my world
I am not what I have achieved, I do make an impact and my contribution is valued
I am not my ego stroked by doing an important job or being in a certain position
I am not Fatmea – she is part of me and perhaps is one of the 'masks' – one of the protective layers keeping the real me hidden or stopping people getting closer or as someone once said to me – let more love inside and you won't need to eat and drink so much!

Boy, it's taken over 50 years to find out who I am – wrong!! I will continue to change and therefore continue to ask, who am I really?

29.09.2005   Day 7

I was born in 1954 – shortly after rationing was fully over! Most of my first 10 years – I was brought up in a house attached to a corner shop – the equivalent of today's supermarket only 1000 times smaller. Fighting for parental attention was a theme as I had 4 sisters and mum and dad both worked in the shop – open all hours!! Nanna and Grandad lived at the bottom of the street and Aunty Mary a few doors down, so the extended family worked well. In a corner shop – food and sweets were never in short supply and it seems that Sunday lunches turned into a competition between me and my dad – could he fill my plate to the extent that I couldn't eat any more! I won every time.

Memorable family outings revolved around picnics – I remember meat pie, boiled eggs, apple pie. Family holidays were mainly Butlins Holiday Camp – all food laid on! So, early influences can set behaviour traits today – recognising them and changing them is part of the battle of me being fully aware and in charge of what I choose to do.

I never really knew my father – he was too busy in the shop – then when the business went bust, he found a job that took him away from home most of the time. He worked on oil rigs as a materials man and was originally one month on, one month off – then it went to 3 months away, then 6 – and at one point, I think he was away for a year. Never really knew what he was up to, but I suspect he had another life.

Some see him as a loveable rogue who dined out on his war stories of being shot down from his Halifax bomber with Christopher Cheshire (Sir Leonard Cheshire's brother. Sir Leonard Cheshire was a decorated World War II veteran and British pilot, who devoted his post-war life to establishing housing and support services for disabled people world-wide). So my father was a prisoner of war for 4 years – from age of 20 to 24.

There are many things we love our parents for and many thins we blame our parents for. Better to let go and forgive than carry grievance and bitterness.

Forgiveness is, I believe, another wonder and miracle of life. It is one of the paths to peace. The opposite is anger which can lead to retribution and war. If we all forgave and stopped putting a claim on what we think is ours – then living in peace is possible. A Nirvana of a community genuinely sharing what we have in common rather than fighting about differences. Now, what's all this got to do with Fatmea and I? Well, the same principle applies to self. I mean we have to learn to live with ourselves. To do this we need to be comfortable with who we are and ideally to love who we are. This may require forgiving yourself for things you may have done in the past. Now, if you were brought up as a Catholic (more of that little chestnut later) you will have a lot to forgive yourself as sin and guilt played a big part in the belief system. So, again, you choose to do what you do out of your awareness at that time – I have moved on, it's passed, let it go. Forgive yourself and celebrate your strengths and the shining qualities that make you and others smile!

THOUGHT FOR THE DAY
Judge less yourself, celebrate being you – judge less of others. (It's a cheap way of feeling superior to others) If you live with criticism, you become a critic!

30.09.2005　Day 8

Have you noticed the more you eat the bigger you get? Your appetite increases so you eat more? There's something wrong between the head and the stomach communication here. We are supposed to eat for a physiological purpose – ie: the body needs nourishment, but because we eat for so many other reasons; habits, comfort, pleasure – because it's there, we tend to stop listening to what our body needs.

In my case, Fatmea is still winning. I eat and drink particularly for pleasure – socially or whilst watching TV. When eating a meal, if I stopped eating when I had a sense of fullness in my stomach, I would probably leave a lot on my plate.

So, time to experiment.

Give my sense of hunger a rating – or better still listen to my stomach which dominates Fatmea and if the message is full – not hungry, then I stop eating.

So 5 = too full, uncomfortable, piggish, greed
   4 = very full – enough
   3 = just right – time to stop
   2 = could probably eat a bit more but if I want to loose weight I should stop
   1 = hungry – definitely need something to eat.

Listening to myself and what my body is telling me is really important. I have often, in the past, pushed myself to the extreme – whether it's work or exercise, I seem to have difficulty with moderation. What was I trying to prove – I guess achievement, whether this is status, income, qualifications, running a marathon – they were all important to me then. Now I have these medals what do I do with them? Have they made me a better person? I think my rich past experiences have certainly coloured my personality and my outlook, but essentially they are not who I am, nor important in the great scheme of things.

So, what is the 'great scheme of things'? I have always believed that my life has a purpose – I believe everyone has. For me, a worthwhile quest is to discover that purpose. I believe I now know what it is?

THOUGHT FOR THE DAY
When you listen to your body what does it say? Can we respond with care and respect for us as a whole person? What is your purpose in life?

01.10.2005   Day 9

Have you noticed that when you start to lose a little weight the apron of fat around your middle gets softer – it wobbles more! I think this is a good sign, in fact when you get to a stage when you can get hold of it with your hands – then as I do – grab it, give it a shake and say

– Fatmea, enjoy it while it lasts – cos you are going!

Keep looking in that mirror and see your fat self then imagine – take off three, maybe four stone – how much better that would look and feel. Even though you have a bad day with Fatmea – ie: she wins on eating and drinking for pleasure (which is pretty even stevens here in Florida on holiday at the moment) don't give up, every day is a new day – the first day of the rest of your life!

We met a lovely couple yesterday – our golfing partners for the day. It's amazing that even as strangers if you wish you can quietly connect – we were open, warm, friendly and they were too and after the game almost exchanged our life stories – and hey – both second marriages, round the same time, their kid a little older than ours but we seem to have a lot in common regards values and outlook in life – and they want to meet us again; who knows, they could turn out to be real good friends.

I believe a lot of relationships are formed through 'giving'. Giving is another wonder of the world. To give time, attention, love and support is within our power and it costs little but means everything to some if given at the right time, with the right attention. In our meeting as strangers – each couple was freely giving genuine interest to each other, enjoying the entertainment of hearing about each other – there was no competition or effort to control – just being with each other.

If you are comfortable with yourself, people will pick this up, if you have little need to prove yourself, impress or impose your status in any way – then the way is open for mutual exploring of each others' world. I believe we (the human race) are all connected – part of the same family – from the same source. Paying attention to each other with love and respect will soon show us we have more in common than differences.

THOUGHT FOR THE DAY
What you pay attention to will grow.
(Apart from Fatmea who is going to shrink – but in this case, it's our health that will grow – improve.)

02.10.2005   Day 10

Help help, my two children are inside, we think they are locked in with a burglar!! The woman, who was a small American, was screeching, partly at me and I guess also to the person on the phone. I instinctively approached the house, torch in hand, belly hanging over my shorts – not sure what to find. This giant of a man marched towards me – 'has the alarm gone off?' I say nonchalantly. He shouts 'yes – what's the frigging code?' The woman shouts back 878 – he puts the code in – the alarm stops. 'Is everything OK now?' – I'm ignored. I retreat. It's 12.30am. Our new American neighbours, it seems, were in a panic. I may get the courage later to ask them what happened. On reflection, what the hell was I doing? Approaching a house at night with panicky strangers – what if it had been a hostage situation – what if the big guy had been a burglar, armed as well – but the instinct to help your fellow human is strong, yes? That's not always the case though. Something can happen in your own head that tells you to protect yourself – you can deny what you see – it happened to me years ago – it linked to a near death experience, but hey – enough for now.

We watched a video last night – essentially, it was about the power of prejudice and this one mans story of how he denied his roots and family in order to progress in society. He was living a lie and eventually recognised he was essentially a victim, a prisoner of his own prejudice. For me, it says something about the importance of knowing who you are in terms of where you came from, a sense of history, generations of development. Somewhere in the spirits of the Universe, my great- great-grandparents are smiling proudly on me - yes – I am proud of my roots – there has to be more good than bad.

My family tree, especially on my Mothers' side is classed in genealogy terms as 'pedigree' – ie: a fare share of well noted citizens over generations in one city – in my case, York, North Yorkshire, United Kingdom.

The most famous being George Walker Milburn, the sculptor.

My fathers' side – well he had a lot of uncles – one of which went to Canada in the very early 1900's and spurned a large family, and we are now in contact with our cousin there. The Wash's apparently congregate from the South – Essex – not inbred Northerners (as we like to think we are) – we think there is some connection to servitude to Royalty somewhere – hence our coat of arms!

This search for roots can be interesting but also a distraction to the real question of 'who you are'. I am unique as everyone is – this is the miracle of humanity – no two people are the same, even identical twins have their differences. Discovering this uniqueness, not being trapped by the past and celebrating who you are, feeling good about yourself is all good medicine in the battle with Fatmea. As a friend once said to me:

THOUGHT FOR THE DAY
I am infinitely valuable and therefore so are you.

03.10.2005   Day 11

Do you eat to live or live to eat? I think most of my life I have been living to eat! Most important events, social events, family occasions have all been associated with making food and drink a big deal. Christmas especially is a period of significant overindulgence. If we have guests for dinner or a party – I see it as my personal job or quest to ensure that everyone's glass is always full. And now, certainly for the past 30 years, I have been on and off diets – so food again has dominated.

So, I think I have had it the wrong way round. It's not live to eat – it's eat to live – doh!!!

I need to reduce the importance and the regularity of those few moments of oral satisfaction – I need to remind myself of the consequences of keeping stuffing Fatmea – I have to deny her and concentrate on the other things in my life than food!!

The beauty of not being on a specific diet is that you don't have to think too much about food. You just eat what you want when you want to. The secret is to want less!

An interesting experiment could be to count how many times you think of food. They say as a young man, men think about sex 100 times a day – for me it was food – perhaps I should have had more sex?!? Now, there's a thought and maybe a topic for later debate?

So, record on a piece of paper a tick or a cross every time you think of food, and when – and the trigger – what set it off?

Then over time, target yourself to reduce this, easier said than done, the power of thought is amazing – so to stop food dominating – it must be replaced by something else – what?

I'm going to try and have a mix of the following every time there is a hint of food thought – the following must dominate:

- picture myself with my grandchildren at Disney
- playing golf for the next 30 years with my wife
- being pain free in my joints.

So,

THOUGHT FOR THE DAY
Imaging and think hard enough about what you want
– you will get it!!

04.10.2005   Day 12

'She broke my 12 string guitar – the bitch – so I am just getting ready to go to her' – the long haired, greasy looking middle aged guy downs a double whiskey – slams it back on the bar and shouts 'set em up gal' – it's happy hour. Our local steak house is a great place for meeting characters. He was sat next to me and I made the gesture, as I do to most people who I sit next to, of saying hi or making comment – I asked him if he was a whiskey drinker and then I got the story of how he fell out with his wife. Then more disturbingly, he went on to tell me his hobby of collecting guns or firearms as he called it. Jo was particularly proud of owning the largest ever made hand gun – so large – he was not allowed to fire it at the local fire range. So he went to the woods last month – fired it in the air and his wrist still hurts! He showed me his ID card that gave him the right to carry a firearm, but also explained that each state is different. In Florida, there has to be 3 movements before it is fired – he keeps his in his glove compartment in the car, so 1, open compartment, 2, take it out and 3 safety catch off and away we go! On Jo's leather jacket, he had about 100 badges or pins – I asked what they were about – he replied - my life story - I said well, it was good talking to you Jo, you go easy now and turned to re-engage with the other conversation my wife was having with a retired American couple on our right. It wasn't long before we got into whether we should pull out of Iraq or not. The consensus was yes - sooner rather than later - control was not going to solve the problem and civil war was inevitable. Do we have a moral responsibility to support - yes we do - but not by giving up our own boys lives - let's find other ways to support the process of peace. It turned out that this couple were Jewish and had strong views on where all this started and the Israel Palestine issue came up. Well, Israel pulling out of Gaza may not be the solution, but it's a start - where do the Israelis / Jews live - with that, their family arrived and a heavy discussion was abated.

I believe in someway we are all connected and there is a reason why things happen. Coincidences are all around us, and if we take the courage, time, effort to enquire, observe and engage, then it is amazing what connections and meanings can be found in our experience of each other.

My conversation with Jo disturbed me and reminded me of the only time I have ever seen a gun fired in anger. It was in Los Angeles - I heard a noise whilst trying to sleep in my hotel - I got up and looked out of the window - I saw a man dressed in a white gown, shouting at a woman - to get in the car - the car was about to drive away, the man dressed in white took out a gun and fired two shots, the woman just managed to get into the car - losing her shoe in the process. It then raced away, it went quiet, I stood there - shocked. I couldn't believe what I had seen - what do I do? Report it, find out what's going on? It was so quiet now I thought someone else will be seeing to it, so I went back to sleep.

The following morning, I wondered if it had been real. I doubted it - maybe I had been dreaming (no one reported anything or had seen anything) - so I went outside the hotel where I saw the shooting - found the shoe and two empty cartridges.

I reported it - eventually, the hotel police took notice but said if there is no body or reported injury, then it's a non-event!

The point to me is that it remains so vivid - how can anyone shoot with the intention of ending a life - a life so precious, a life so miraculous, yet so fragile.

05.10.2005   Day 13

Fatmea won yesterday – big blow out on beer, wine and snacks! Why? Not sure – it was a grey rainy day all day – we did some housework and shopping – no golf – maybe it was something to do with – not had my fair share of pleasure today – if it was – then I have missed the plot again! Pleasure should be in the breath we breathe, the things we see and the experience of being free and loving. OK – yes – but – no buts – no excuses – what got me was old habits, rituals, one too many drinks and the old 'in your mouth snacked out game' comes into play.

Admitting old patterns and recognising them when they come into play is important. OK – so, what will today bring? We have 3 days left of our holiday – usually, I put on ½ stone in weight in a typical Florida binge – this time I hope to have not put any weight on – not lost any either – so big weigh in when we get back – gulp!

Having realistic goals is important and losing weight within a reasonable length of time rather than within weeks will also help the body to adjust more permanently to its change. Losing weight quickly leaves you vulnerable to putting it back on the first time you eat a little above the equation E in < E out.

Most mornings I manage to do 20 minutes aerobic exercise – either on my exercise bike here or my cross trainer at home. It really is the minimum – I used to do a lot more. I used to be a referee in Rugby Union for about 4 seasons until my knee gave way. It's the greatest game on earth to referee – you're so involved and you get great respect for getting the balance between control, shaping the game and decision making right. There's a phrase as a referee you shout out in the match to help the game move – it's when the ball is held by one team in a 'maul' (group of guys bunched together holding the ball). They must be moving forward – if they become still for too long then the ref shouts 'use it or lose it' – then they have 3 seconds to pass the ball or it becomes a penalty.

I think we also have a life principle here - if you stay still too long - you lose the ability to move. Use it or lose it - refers to our body and faculties.

So, if you don't exercise - you end up as an immovable, stiff blob. If you don't think, test your mind, experience new things, learn - then your brain turns to mush.

THOUGHT FOR THE DAY
Use it or lose it.

06.10.2005   Day 14

Our last final day on holiday here in Sunny Florida. In fact, the last few days have been very cloudy with a lot of rain - we are on the tail end of tropical storm Tammy. Cute names for storms - hurricane Katrina claimed New Orleans and many lives - the power of unrelenting natural phenomena such as storms and earthquakes - the Tsunami - it's an amazing and scary planet, an unfathomable world. Are these storms getting worse, more frequent because of global warming and are we contributing towards this as a result of the way we live and consume. I think it is better to err on the side of caution and say - for the sake of argument - we can not afford to play roulette with our planet. For the sake of our grandchildren's children, we need to start taking care a little more. Recycling and being a little more conscious about the energy we use is a start.

I am a great believer in 'you get what you give', 'you reap what you sow' - if we take care of the planet - it will take care of us, if we give love and attention, it will be returned, if you want to lose weight and get fit then help others to do the same.

Bill was a big Scottish golfer who took a great interest in how we managed our Villa - he asked us for a card and we gave him some helpful tips and pitfalls to avoid. We then started talking about golf generally and I mentioned that I was talking to an American called Sterling the other day, who built golf courses and was working with Jack Nicklaus - Bill then handed me a Scottish £5 pound note - on one side was Jack Nicklaus holding the St Andrew's cup - now what happens next was the weird thing - he said 'keep it'! Just hold that moment – a Scotsman giving money away – I showed my shock – and he said – you will appreciate that, being a Yorkshire man – you see Scotsmen and Yorkshire men have this reputation of being somewhat frugal! A generous gesture and one that secures that meeting in my mind forever. Thanks Bill.

We have a reaction to everyone we meet – it's difficult to hide that reaction as our non-verbal cues give it away – our smile, frown, tone of voice, eye contact immediately communicate – do you want to engage with this person? Also, internally your feelings will start to indicate positively or negatively – we begin to make assumptions, begin to judge. These assumptions and judgements say more about us than the people we meet. Our reaction to others is based on our own insecurities, history, experience, prejudice and fears. Never judge a book by its cover is a great saying and one that applies here. This also applies to ourselves. When we look in the mirror what do we see? Do we see Fatmea dominating and therefore you don't like what you see – or do you see beyond this? The celebration of who you are with all your gifts, talents, the unique characteristics that make 'you' you. The miraculous way the body works, where each cell communicates with every other cell, and each one dies naturally to allow new growth so every day you are changing.

Think about it – how different you look compared to ten, twenty, thirty, forty years ago – wow – isn't it incredible the way we grow.

THOUGHT FOR THE DAY
Loving and accepting who we are will be evident in a
warmth that radiates when engaging with other people.

07.10.2005   Day 15

Last night of the holiday – Fatmea's last meal of its type, ie: eating whilst at level 5! ie: eating whilst full until uncomfortable – it's strange – this time, I know I was doing it. I was watching myself and almost in a slow motion video saying to Fatmea – as if on the night before her death sentence – farewell – no more – that's it!!

Mave, my wife, said to me yesterday – you're like all those tradesmen, painters, builders who find they have to do jobs for everyone else but tend to put their own house in order last. Well – time to put my home first and I am really looking forward to a new me.

I read the other day about an experiment between two groups of patients with cancer. They were both given conventional treatment but one group, in addition, formed a support group to listen to each other, explore their feelings and expressing their fears and doubts. After a year, the group in the support group's recovery rate was significantly better. I believe healing processes are enhanced through the power of thought and its expression. This book is my way of doing this, but I can see that the various 'diet groups' who come together use this principle too. It's not the special diet; it's the experiences of support and the encouragement that goes with it.

Some would go as far as saying the power of prayer – or thinking positive thoughts for others – also helps. I believe there has also been an experiment where this has been proven. The point here is that when embarking upon a life change – it's better to have open, positive support and a channel where you can express your thoughts and feelings. This will help you be in touch with your feelings. Feelings are the biggest clue to what's going on inside yourself, what's the issue, express it, let it out, learn to love what ever it is that's trying to get out. This is all about acceptance and knowing who you are. Let those around you, who love you, help you. Now – that was the builder with the half built house talking. I know the theory, I know the psychology, physiology, biology, but the 'ology' of applying to myself – I still have to graduate!

When waking each morning I am gong to pause. My prayer will be:-

Thank God for another day, help me be fully aware of everything going on inside and outside me so I can consciously choose how to spend that moment.

I wonder what today's surprise will be? Each new experience adds something to our lives and if we can catch that moment – it's enhanced and enriched. Every day will present a new experience if we are sufficiently alert to it. To do this we have to be in touch with our own feelings, follow through on our own intuition and have the courage to check out those coincidences. Doing this will fill us, our appetite for life will be satisfied to the extent we will not need to overeat.

THOUGHT FOR THE DAY
Be conscious in every moment, breathe deeply and
recognise your connection with everything around you and
the fact that you are creating this moment.

08.10.2005   Day 16

Back home in the UK! Now for the weigh in - 240 lbs! That's not bad at all. A loss of 5lbs on holiday in Florida, when I usually come back at least 7lbs heavier! And I ate and drank what I wanted - OK - also had 20 minutes aerobic exercise each morning and we played golf most days so high energy but, also drank beer and wine and had snacks every night. Started the day with a breakfast cereal and orange juice or had a brunch. We occasionally had a hot dog for lunch but mostly missed lunch out. In the evening, by the time I had had a few beers and a starter, I only had room for half a meal, so Mave and I would share or do without. It didn't feel as if I was depriving myself - it felt right. In fact - the few occasions where we had a starter and a meal - it was too much!!

So, now to focus on some healthy eating. A bit more veg, which seems in short supply in American Restaurants.

THOUGHT FOR THE DAY
We are what we eat.

09.10.2005   Day 17

Have you ever noticed when certain individuals enter your space, the energy changes. I believe we are all affected by each others' 'energy field' and this energy field is largely to do with our personality and how confident and comfortable we are with ourselves, but also can be affected by what we eat.

Most children are high energy influencers – they demand attention, they affect our mood immediately, their energy is high, their behaviour spontaneous and reactions genuine. They have very little baggage to suppress their real selves and to see rapid growth, learning and their delight in front of our eyes is a real joy. Their bodies are also very sensitive and it is a well established fact that if you give a child certain foods, particularly those with additives, then they can have a significant effect on their ability to concentrate. If it's the same for children, why does it have to stop when we reach adulthood? I don't think it does. I think it's important to understand how certain types of food affect our energy levels and mood. For example, I know if I have a good meal which involves high carbohydrates and a few beers, my reaction is: feet up and a snooze.

If I have my main meal at 8pm, I want to sleep at 10.30pm. However, if I have a light meal at 6pm and a snack at 8pm, I'm OK til 12. So timing and eating in a way that suits your body clock or body's natural rhythm is also a factor. It's all about tuning in to what your body needs, rather than feeding your emotional self around social events, it's being aware of why you are eating and for what purpose. I know if I don't have something for my breakfast by 10.30am, my concentration and ability to think is reduced.

If you really wanted to get into this and find out how food affects you, you could keep a diary of what you eat and then on the column beside this, note how you feel in both mood and energy. It's amazing what patterns emerge.

Now, back to 'energy fields'. In essence, all we are as humans are DNA (our human identity kit) cells and the particles (atoms) that make up those cells packaged together and vibrating as a field of energy. In addition to this, I believe we have a soul and spirit but more of that later. When humans come together their energy fields interact. Try an experiment – watch how peoples' mood, attention and body posture changes when certain individuals enter the room, or, if you can – watch how they react to you.

If you, or the new person entering the room, are high energy, positive, stimulating – then so will the group be – if you are depressed, negative – then this will also impact or drain away others energy.

I still believe that fundamentally the way to lose weight is to ensure that energy out is greater than energy in, however, maybe there is a way to increase energy out by eating certain foods at times your body is best equipped to digest and use the food.

Every person is unique and has different needs. The principle is finding out and being in touch with what your body needs and wants and responding appropriately. This is important in the journey of awareness and taking charge of your life.

Have you also noticed that when two people are in love, the energy they have for each other is visible, indeed, if this love is intense then you can almost see the warmth, the energy field, even sparks between them. This is evidence of another 'food' available to us. Giving and receiving love is a source of energy so the more you engage in loving relationships that are healthy, balanced and free, the less you will want to eat.

I need to receive more, giving is easy, and I enjoy it. Receiving, for some reason, is more difficult. I have been a carer, a giver all my life, and perhaps because it has been out of balance I have compensated with food. Time to put that balance right.

THOUGHT FOR THE DAY
My body is the most sophisticated and complex
communication system in the World. Its intelligence is far
greater than any computer – how can I tap into and listen
to its' wisdom?

10.10.2005   Day 18

30,000+ people dead in an Earthquake in Pakistan – it's difficult to imagine – villages and small towns destroyed – lives just gone. What with famine and war in Africa, war in Iraq, the Tsunami, Hurricane hurricane Katrina and now the prospect of a pandemic of Bird Flu – it seems the human race is under attack from all sides. Most of the aforementioned are natural disasters, but some are human disasters such as the incompetence of government in Africa, the incompetence of Charity relief to get the money where it is needed fast and the futility of war as an option to solve disputes over power and control.

I remember as a young father when my two sons were toddlers

how anxious I was about the prospect of World annihilation through nuclear war between USA and Russia. I used to plan and work out how to build a shelter in the garden and what supplies I would need to protect my family.

At that time also, in the early 1980's – there was the first sign that a virus called HIV / AIDS was going to devastate the Western population as at that time – it was totally untreatable. As it happens it did, and is devastating the population, but not the richer nations – Africa is dying of AIDS.

I didn't sleep well last night (body trying to readjust – different time zone) and I woke with these thoughts. It all seems to put my battle with Fatmea into perspective. At one level, talking about losing weight and getting healthier seems trivial compared to the World disasters and traumas, yet at another level – it makes it even more important. You see, I am so fortunate to live a life of relative luxury and wealth. I have all the advantages and opportunities to do what's right for myself and others. To throw this away by eating and drinking myself to an early grave seems criminal! If every individual took time to seek peace within themselves – then perhaps some of the human-made disasters could be prevented.

Today we were all under threat due to the will of fanatical individuals who are willing to die for their cause but intend taking those without real choice with them – the so called suicide bombers. This was brought home to me whilst working in London on 21st July this year, two weeks after 52 people died in the London Underground and Bus bombings. I was working for a company in Hammersmith and my wife came with me for a little tourist break. During the morning in one of the offices, the news broke – another bomb on the underground. I knew my wife Mave was out there somewhere. Thank god for mobile phones. I was able to contact her – I tried to reassure her it was a minor incident but better to get back to the hotel – don't use the underground – get a taxi or walk. Half an hour later, I rang again – where was she? On the underground towards Hammersmith where the incident was!! She said there were no taxis, she got a bus but it went the wrong way – she asked someone and they said the underground was OK and still open – everywhere was cordoned off and she had difficulty finding a route back to the hotel. Thank god these were the failed bombs. On our journey home on a packed train from London to York – you could feel the tension in the air. When the guardsman announced a request for someone to claim a bag in one of the carriages the silence and the eye contact between us all spoke volumes.

THOUGHT FOR THE DAY
Life is precious and vulnerable, it could end any minute
– let's look after it and celebrate each moment we have and
pray for those who don't have this opportunity.

11.10.2005   Day 19

Well, so far so good. Back to work, catching up with emails, loads of reading and preparing for meetings etc. Keeping off the snacks and booze – should see some reduction this week.

Watched some golf last night. Saw John Daly lose against Tiger Woods in the American Express World Championship. He lost in a play-off – he needed to hole a 2½ foot putt to stay in – he missed. It was an easy shot but I guess under those circumstances the pressure is great. John has also got a significant relationship with his 'Fatmea' and has struggled over the years with many demons. I wonder what demon jumped on his back then when he bent down to take the putt?

Watching the great champions of golf and listening to them when interviewed says something about how they are with the game and themselves – you can list them all – Arnold Palmer, Jack Nicklaus, Sevy Ballesteros, Tiger Woods, plus many others – these are people who are in control of their 'ego' – their external identity or outer selves – how people see them, their status.

Whereas those that are either almost there, not quite up with the greats or once was great, but fall into drugs, booze or dysfunctional relationships are ego dominant, that is – they depend on their external image, their status for satisfaction, fame, power, control and relationships. All of which are transitory, short lived and superficial. Greatness comes from within and is congruent with ones beliefs and behaviour. This is also true for achieving success in a long lasting way – so losing weight just to look good for others will, in the long run, not be a good enough reason to keep the weight off. Personally, looking good is along way down the list of reasons for losing weight – it's a benefit – not a reason. The reasons are clear – to live a longer, healthier life – to be fit as long as possible, to enjoy and continue to thrive with and learn more about the miracle of life.

> ***THOUGHT FOR THE DAY***
> ***When faced with a 2½ foot putt, think ball in the hole – not self missing.***
> ***Our bodies are a product of our awareness – our mind and body are inseparable – they are one. We are what we think – think deep from within – not what others want to see.***
> ***Be ourselves, be genuine and true.***

12.10.2005   Day 20

Watched Pride of Britain last night. One of the obvious winners was Jane Tomlinson – diagnosed with terminal cancer five years ago – given six months to live. Since then, she has raised £1,000,000 by running marathons, cycling across Europe, completed the Iron Man (Women's) Challenge. She is the living proof that mind can heal the body. Her positive attitude and determination is an inspiration to us all. So, if you were given six months to live – would you go for a run?

Throughout our lives, we are going to be faced with many dark challenges – and it is at these times, we need to remind ourselves that we still have the power to choose. We can choose to be subsumed by the darkness, or be positive and work through it in the best way we can.

This was always an early message I gave to my two boys (they are both now 27) in the context of Star Wars – the film. Essentially a battle between good and evil, darkness and light – 'may the force be with you' we used to say to each other. A little like a blessing 'God be with you'.

Any journey of change, whether it's changing job, new house or losing weight will present its challenges, doubts and frustrations. At these times, it is important to remind oneself of what's important.

Going back over this diary and re-reading it from time to time helps to reinforce some of the insights and commitment needed to carry on.

THOUGHT FOR THE DAY
When you seek money or power for the sake of your ego,
you spend money chasing the illusion of happiness instead
of enjoying happiness in the moment.

13.10.2005   Day 21

My sister leaves to live in Spain this week. (I already have one sister living out there).

I guess the attraction is the warmer climate and cheaper cost of living for those retiring or near retirement age. It takes courage to uproot yourself and leave your home town. I remember when I changed career at the age of 30 it required moving me and my family down south 200 miles to a relatively new town called Milton Keynes. Before I left I walked the streets of York recalling every memory associated with every corner.

Letting go of what's familiar can seem a little like grieving. The difference is you can always return. Combine this sense of loss with entering the unknown can, on one hand, be nerve wracking or/and exciting as anticipating a great adventure.

Losing a significant amount of weight – saying goodbye to a familiar part of yourself, ie: Fatmea, can also be seen like an adventure. How different will I feel? How will people respond to me? What new opportunities will it bring? All reactions and questions that could be appropriate as if we were moving to Spain!

I will miss my sister, I love her to bits. I have 3 sisters, we are very close – always were and drawn together even more through adversity – loss of Mum tragically in an accident and my younger sister Veronica who died of kidney failure at the age of 25. We used to get together quite often – but this triggered off our memories and grief – then after a while, we realised that getting together should be a celebration of what we have had and what we have got. Not what trauma we share.

So, a session with the 3 sisters who are more extrovert than I am can be quite an affair!! They will kill me for saying this – but I suppose we are all a little overweight. One rationalisation could be – it's in the genes – and yes – when you look at our parents, aunties, uncles – none of them were built slight and some of them were quite round. Personally – I don't believe it follows, ie: fat parents = fat child from a biological point of view.

It's more likely to be the child copies the behaviours of the parents, which includes the eating habits.

We inherit a lot from our parents, including values, behavioural traits, likes, fears and interests. I think it is important to know what these are and to what extent they influence you today – and then choose whether this is what you want – so they are yours, and not something you associate with being uncontrollable.

From my father, I have entrepreneurship, risk taking and a competitive spirit. The latter, I am not sure I like and have battled with it from time to time – more of that later I think. From my mum, well – caring, sensitivity, giver, spiritual qualities and from both – a sense of humour and fun. These are positive qualities I can relate to, but there are others I have worked hard at diminishing – from mum – sense of guilt (Catholic upbringing) with many should and should not's – also easy to get into a victims way of thinking. From my father – perhaps his stubbornness.

So this journey is associated with farewell to Fatmea, is also saying hello to the real you. The real 'me' – Mike, Michael, Mikey, Michael G Wash – where are you?

I guess we all hide from time to time – life ain't a rehearsal though – so let's get this show on the road!

THOUGHT FOR THE DAY
We may seek warmer climates abroad – but nothing can substitute the warmth that radiates from within.

14.10.2005   Day 22

On my own last night. My step-daughter took her mum to London to see our favourite show Les Miserables, for a birthday treat. My son came round early evening to talk through his work situation. He has just gone independent as a sales consultant – brave step – it's good he can come round and talked through his dilemmas and concerns.

Two of my sisters and their partners are here tonight to give one of them a send off to live in Spain and we are babysitting my grandson. It's important to be with family in an environment of love and fun. It's important to listen to each other, but recognise in the end you must take your own counsel.

The last time I listened to my Mother was after she had died – about 5 years after. My testicle had swollen up – I thought nothing at the time – I had been running quite a bit – in training for a half marathon and my balls had got caught in a hole in my underpants I discovered after a run – and they were sore for a while. It was shortly after this they became swollen. I ignored it for several weeks – then one night I had a dream – the only time I have heard and seen my Mother in a dream – she basically was pleading for me to go to the Doctors – it was so vivid – I woke – went to the Doctors – and was admitted to hospital the following day and the day after I was Michael Ivor Bollockoff!!

Lesson here – sometimes it pays to listen to those closest to you whether they are dead or alive! It also says something about the powers of the conscious and unconscious mind. Consciously I was denying I had something wrong with me – unconsciously – the message came through in my dreams. What I am doing here with this diary is increasing my conscious awareness and bringing from what may be hidden in the unconscious or difficult, to admit out into the open.

So, I cannot hide from, or deny the fact that I am overeating and drinking myself to an early grave which is a direct contradiction to what I want in life.

Face it, think about it, then do something about it. In long journeys it's good sometimes to reinforce ones commitment and remind oneself of what this is really about. Farewell to Fatmea is a protracted goodbye but one that is certain. Determination and persistence are qualities that are also needed here.

The other thought today relates to dreams. I believe dreams are a significant part of us. They are our unconscious self acting out in creative and weird ways. In each dream there is a message – it's for us to put meaning into these dreams and find the message – no psychologist or theory can do that for us. Sometimes, during significant change we dream more vividly (as long as you are not suppressed by drugs or booze) –if you want to work on your dreams have a pen and paper by your bed, when you wake up write down the images or story that's still in your head – if you don't, mostly they are forgotten in moments unless someone or something breaks the dream and it comes flooding back. You can then reflect and put your own meaning on to it. By the way, you can choose to be positive or negative in your interpretation – but why would anyone choose to be negative. One night I dreamt I was in callipers – aids to help me walk as I had something seriously wrong with my legs – in the dream I was getting upset because they kept going loose and breaking – my interpretation was – even though I was upset this was about me breaking free – away from Fatmea – being more mobile and wearing out those callipers.

THOUGHT FOR THE DAY
We are more than our conscious self – what lies beneath is
a wealth of insights and learning about who we really are.
We just need to stop a while – listen. No – really stop – and
really listen!

15.10.2005   Day 23

The big weigh in today. Once a week is enough – weighing daily is meaningless because of daily fluctuations in water and weight varies depending on time of day so same time each week gives a better indication of real weight loss. My step-daughter, who is 21 and in her final year at University, is a young inspiration and example of how to lose weight – she has been successful I believe because she has combined three fundamental things – sensible eating, exercise and personal development. The latter involving her on a journey of self discovery which study and experience at University has helped. She will be coming round today to see how I have done as she has challenged me to lose 14lbs before Christmas. I suspect I have lost two or three pounds this week, although I did have an Indian curry and glass of wine for dinner in celebration of seeing my sister off to Spain last night and a BLT for lunch - so who knows - let's see!

Woke up this morning clutching my crucifix and thinking about Father Mortell - why? I don't know - Father Mortell was the priest I used to serve when I was an alter boy. From the age of 8 to 13, I used to attend daily mass and support the Catholic ritual. I remember it was a privilege and honour and can't recall never resenting it or thinking I wish I wasn't doing it. I always remember it as a great way to start the day. I felt good (or was it God) inside. These early influences led me into thinking perhaps my vocation was one that involved a life time of dedication. So, at thirteen, I joined St Cassians Novitiate which was a boarding school for

training De La Salle Brothers - a catholic teaching order. Again, great memories and a great education. My first real experiences of learning the value of reflection through prayer and meditation. I stayed until I was 15 and something told me - this wasn't for me. It was a realisation that I could serve God in the community through my own family and work and also at the time I wanted to support my Mother - who with Father away as usual, was having a rough time looking after my sisters, of which one had just had a child out of wedlock (gosh that sounds old fashioned) - which for a catholic parent was a bit tricky!

So, why Father Mortell - he died recently I know and I am so pleased that last Easter I went back to my old Church, and he spoke to me after mass - he remembered me, my mum (he called her by her first name Frances) and the corner shop. It felt like coming home!

Many people dismiss their religion and I guess I did for a time. But once you have worked through negative issues such as institutionalised guilt - and then looked at the symbols, metaphors, stories and history as opportunities to give your life meaning, then it can be part of the overall journey towards enlightenment.

I don't go to church regularly - just when I feel like it - perhaps I'm building up to a visit? Maybe pray for my sisters' success in Spain and maybe pray for myself and my continued commitment to say farewell to Fatmea?

THOUGHT FOR THE DAY
Is there more to this life than what we can see or feel and can we tap into it?

16.10.2005   Day 24

Loss of 5lbs this week! Not bad since all I have done is cut down on the booze, no crisps/nuts, cut down on cheese, bread, and pasta but essentially – I ate what I wanted – when I wanted – the difference – awareness and commitment to change, to lose Fatmea. This has resulted in it feeling easy. Something switches in the head and heart and determination, combined with understanding the long term and permanent nature of what I want to achieve has helped me so far. I know the first 14lbs or so are relatively easy and after that I may have to reduce my intake even further and up the exercise a little. Well, if you think about it – I am getting smaller therefore given a stable energy output – I would have to eat less and less to keep reducing as a smaller machine needs less fuel, yes? So from 245lbs to 235lbs in 25 days (14 days of which were holiday time in Florida!). My target realistically I believe should be below or at 200lbs (14st 4lbs) with a life long commitment to never go over that again. When I will achieve this I don't know – let's see what happens! No, let's make it happen! To do this I must continue to hold my attention to every moment – know what's going on with me, inside, heart, mind, feelings and my reaction to the world and others at the same time hold with passionate desire by intention to be fit and healthy. This is, I believe, a formulae for success in all walks of life – awareness of the moment combined with a passionate desire for achievement. Great leaders demonstrate this by not accepting the concept of failure – there are set backs, opportunities to learn and take advantage of, so moving forward if anything is enhanced through this experience.

I think diets fail because they are only dealing with one aspect of living – eating choices and behaviour. People do lose weight but most, if not all, eventually put it back on in spades. This is because it hasn't been a fully integrated change – deep down – what's it all about. A desire to lose weight needs to be combined with a desire to know yourself, and to know what you want. The more explicit and clear about what you want in life, the more chance you have of getting it. So, what do I want to achieve? Or better way of putting it – what do I desire – To be 14 stone, to be happy, healthy, relaxed, satisfied with work, have fun, play good golf, to be loved, to love, to be a contributor, to maintain humility and develop wisdom. Wow! –

wouldn't that be something. I guess everybody's list is different but I suspect everyone wants health and happiness but unfortunately other things take over, it ceases to be a conscious desire, not a priority so, eating, drinking, smoking, taking illegal drugs suppress the real desires/wants in life even further. I do feel for those trapped in this vicious circle – some need help to stand back and look at themselves, make real choices and then they need support to follow through on these choices. I don't believe enough is being done for the younger generation to help them realise what the implications of over indulgence in drugs and alcohol is doing to them – nor as a society do we have an alternative culture of a recreational lifestyles without these substances.

What's the answer?

THOUGHT FOR THE DAY
The more passionate and committed you are in achieving what you desire – the easier the journey will be.

17.10.2005   Day 25

Do you think there are more fat men than fat women? I think so! Something to do with from an early age reinforcing the stereotype of it's good to be a big strong man and good to be a petite feminine woman. The number of men walking around with what us Brits call a beer belly – looking quite pregnant – and proud of it – is worrying! Men do tend to put most of their excess fat around the abdomen, yet it seems more acceptable for men to be overweight than women. Yet, most of the diet industry is geared toward women, and if you go to a typical 'weight watchers' meeting, you would be hard pressed to see a man there. I think men have difficulty generally in accepting they need support and help. This macho image of 'I'm OK' and 'I can cope' and 'I want to be strong for others' are messages handed down to us from parents and reinforced through television, film and advertising. It's a load of rubbish of course – men are as in much need for support and help as women.

Men generally get a bad press – I can understand it and have some sympathy with this. Who are the rapists, paedophiles, murderers, war criminals, despots of this world? Vast majority - men,

I don't know if it's in the DNA or genetic make up but there does seem to be a tendency for men to seek power and control - more so than women.

I know these are generalisations and people may shoot me down with researched evidence saying men and women are equal in these matters, but look around you - men are in the vast majority of power and control positions in the World. In most marriages - who is the most dominant partner - men? I believe essentially all relationships or positions dominated by power and control disintegrate.

I know I'm quite a dominant figure and have in the past been very controlling - I like to think this is less and less. I try to be less controlling in my behaviour, for example on holiday, I do two things - I never wear a watch and never have an opinion as to what we should do. I just like to go with the flow - see what happens. It's quite freeing - try it.

A little more difficult in a work situation where I have to plan ahead, be organised and make things happen - but I think it's healthy to be aware of how much and when we try to control. Why? Because it's the source of an unequal relationship - one where the controller drains and takes the energy of another. It has less potential than a relationship based on sharing and mutual understanding, give and take - here energy is exchanged to the extent that the end result is more energy, not less. Energy not wasted by suppressing or controlling people or events.

If you control and dominate, you create dependency. Those who are dependant have far less opportunity to learn, thrive themselves, and therefore it's more difficult for them to realise their full potential.

What's this got to do with losing weight? Well - I believe the same principle applies to a relationship with ourselves.

If you take on a diet, to take control and say to yourself - I'm in charge, I will decide what to eat, I will control my eating and I will beat this thing - then, that sounds like a commitment based on power and control and may disintegrate.

Alternatively, and this is what I am trying here - if you try to understand why you are the way you are, understand and appreciate what you have, and what being 'fat' has done for you (positive and negative) then make a conscious choice to change based on this awareness and understanding, this is a more equal relationship with yourself. One based on love, acceptance and respect, rather than power, and control. You can lose weight, be kind to yourself and enjoy all at the same time.

18.10.2005   Day 26

My first career was in mental health nursing and I have many weird and wonderful stories that I have never told. Some are sad and frightening, others, you wouldn't believe! One event I recall vividly involves 13 year old Melissa. She was quite tall for her age yet weighed only six stone. My job – observation. Make sure she ate and did herself no harm. Meal times were a tortuous affair, lasted over 2 hours, as she would pick the smallest crumb from her plate, take a life time to put it in her mouth and take even longer to swallow it.

She believed the longer the food was exposed to air before she ate – the less it weighed and the more she chewed, the more calories she would burn and take out of the food. If she wasn't observed, she would make herself sick and before she got weighed she would drink water and stuff objects up her rectum to convince us she was putting on weight, so we would leave her alone, so she could go home.

Melissa genuinely thought she was fat, she had low esteem, was depressed, disliked herself and her own image so much she wanted to die – although she wouldn't admit this.

I remember her long blond hair, her blue eyes in dark sunken sockets and her bony fingers and stick-like arms. She spoke in a quiet, gentle whisper of a voice.

It must have been a peculiar sight to see me walk by her side in the garden – I am over 6 feet in height and at that time, a fit young rugby player of 16 stone – it must have looked like something out of a fantasy film.

Melissa also used to self harm – mainly by cutting her arms and legs.

I tell this story because it is an extreme example of how the mind can control our beliefs and our behaviour, by distorting the way life, the world and ourselves are seen.

When you look in the mirror, what do you see? Melissa saw something/someone she abhorred – our job was to help her like – no love herself again. Her parents were well off, very possessive, protective, controlling and there was a history of the mother being depressed, which started to happen after the death of a younger child – Melissa's sister. So, grief, fear of loss, not being able to replace or step into her sisters shoes – all these factors come into play – but at the end of the day, Melissa had to learn to love herself.

Melissa eventually gained weight and was allowed home for weekend leave. She took an overdose of paracetomol and died.

A young life – gone.

The power of the mind.

Could it be that those of us who are obese are in some way like Melissa, but instead of starving ourselves to death – we are eating ourselves to death?

THOUGHT FOR THE DAY
Love what you see, care what you do, be gentle on yourself.

19.10.2005   Day 27

I won a little battle yesterday! In a meeting all day – early start so ate an apple and banana on the way into work. Broke for lunch – someone wanted to meet over lunch – these meetings are intense affairs – I am one of the responsible managers for an organisation on the brink of bankruptcy, so everyone is focussed and each debate is challenging – grab a sandwich and 'let's go' shouts the Chairman. So, off we went, after the lunch meeting we rejoin the main group.

In the room, sandwiches still remain – beautiful ham and cheese salad, beef, chicken on a variety of breads – I approach, my hand moves to grab a plate – then two things happen. I refer to Fatmea – what do you want – I am at Level 2 – could eat more but not if I am going to lose weight – I move closer to the plate, then I ask myself – why?

I remind myself of the vision of golf for the next 30 years, grandchildren time and pain free joints – I win – back to work! These small battles are important, and to be aware of your own behaviour and making conscious decisions is all part of the journey to success.

Talk about journeys! There was a programme on TV last night called 'Beyond Boundaries' – a group of disabled (or differently abled) people taking a route across jungle, desert, mountain terrain one was paralysed, one walking on 2 false legs, another deaf, another blind – I couldn't believe what I was seeing. Witness the pain and the risks – for what? To discover how far they can go, to celebrate the power and strength of the human mind to overcome the limitation of the body, to experience the love and bond created when a team is faced with adversity and need each other to survive.

It's a humbling experience watching this and makes my battle with Fatmea small stuff!

Saddam Hussein goes on trial today – 2 years after the Iraq invasion. Tried for one of many crimes he is accused of but not the gassing of the Kurds in Northern Iraq. They showed the pictures on TV of the women and children lying in the streets after the gas attack – I wept – I cry and despair for our human race. There must be another way. I don't think I will see peace in my time, but I hope I see the path of peace created.

Peace will only be achieved when governments begin to adopt a more spiritual philosophy of life and begin to let go of the need for territory and control. It seems impossible – we need more saints and miracle workers to bring us together as one family, capable of sharing this beautiful planet.

THOUGHT FOR THE DAY
There are no limits, no boundaries, let's start by making peace with ourselves, then our neighbours.

20.10.2005   Day 28

I believe all our relationships are a reflection of the relationship with ourselves. I have very few close friends – and those I have I see rarely. I am not proactive in seeking them out, nor are they to me, but when we meet, it's as if we have never been apart.

I have friendly neighbours, work colleagues and associates – and some of them are quite close. My relationship with my family is one of love and a strong bond with regular communication taking place – very different to friends.

Relationships are about intimacy and how prepared you are to share, disclose, trust and just be with another, enjoying who each of you are. This needs developing and can so easily be broken. I think being overweight can be a barrier to intimacy. If you feel under confident, low esteem and unattractive, then this will affect your presence with others. Some overcome this of course, and make their performance revolve around the 'big personality' for example, our beloved British comedienne – Dawn French. But others shy away, watch more TV and eat more snacks. People would be surprised to hear that given a choice of a party or a film with snacks – the latter works for me! I don't know whether I would have always chosen this, or if this is a recent thing over the last few years. In my work, I have to manage groups, often over 100 in number and perform all day as a facilitator / coach – maybe the TV preference is about resting or, more likely, it's about avoiding having to make an effort talking and listening – sometimes to topics or issues I find difficult getting into and not worth fighting for air time. This has been my experience of parties – I would rather rush round serving everyone drinks than get involved in drunken chit chat – that's what I do eventually, but by then, I've had a few drinks so it doesn't matter.

It's also to do with a value of mine – it's more important to listen than to talk – and going into an interaction, then I am always going to hear more than I say so the opportunity to communicate my point of view or who I am is minimal.

The other issue in this is I don't feel the need to compete with others who want to talk – I have nothing to prove – but it's not about proving anything – it's about meeting. You are more likely to meet if the sharing is equal – also if you really listen you will find a connection that relates to you and is appropriate to share. I think I need to get closer to people I meet – Fatmea leaving me will help, but also, I need to remember that in social situations, the stimulation of really meeting others and enjoying them as people is enough to warrant not getting drunk!

THOUGHT FOR THE DAY
Why are we having this conversation (why are you reading this for that matter)? What is its significance – will we be closer as a result?
What does really meeting someone mean?

21.10.2005   Day 29

Lord of all
Open me
Receive me
Fill me with light
That I might
Be

This was my contract with God. I said this simple prayer in 1988 whilst sitting in St Paul's Cathedral in London. At the time, I was receiving radiology for cancer. I said to God – if I survive – I will serve you. At the time, my idea of God was related to a hope that this invisible intelligent and superior being may just be in some spirit world influencing and controlling things.

I have come to realise since, and now believe that a 'face' doesn't exist and it is part of our current universe – and each of us contribute to it – my God, is the spirit of life and death – it's all pervading, to see God, you have to look closely at a flower, or stand alone in the mountains. Part of our path or journey to realising our full potential is to realise the power of God – we are all potentially leaders as Jesus was, if only we could harness this force as readily as he did. If only each of us could be miracle workers – the world would be a better place.

I came through radiology – OK – two images stay with me – the first is – I am lying totally naked under the machine – this was the marking session. They need to mark out exactly where to focus the x-rays. To do this, they 'spot you' – I was lying there, I can recall several women walking backwards and forwards touching me with cold hands, asking me to move a little here, a little there – totally naked. It was cold. They gave me what they called beauty spots – I still have them today – essentially small tattoos that now look like moles to help the radiographer position appropriately.

The other image – after my first session, which lasts barely 10 minutes – I was surprised, felt no different – it was a sunny day. I walked to the shops before going home. At that time, there was no real advice as to what I should or shouldn't do – I got home and I have never been as sick in my life! I vomited every 10 minutes, I was retching continuously – I was so sore, so frightened – I began to think they had given me an overdose – I thought I had radiation sickness (which, in a way, I did). My insides had been turned outside and my head was painful to burst! After 12 hours or so, it was over. It didn't happen again – nausea and generally ill – but not vomiting.

I remember trying to be sick quietly because I knew my two boys, who were about 5 years old, were downstairs – they must have been worried about their dad.

So God, so far so good – the traumatic death of my mother, the early death of my sister, and now me – yep – I agree – too many. So a pact – 'fill me with light that I might be' and I reckon the less food takes up, the more room for light. To serve God is to serve humanity, do good in this world, be happy and create happiness for others – now that's not a bad purpose for life, is it??

Weigh in day (WID) tomorrow. Not a bad week so far. Kept off the booze and snacks, had a light lunch (sometimes fruit and salad), light cereal to start the day and meat and vegetables for dinner. Still doing 20 minutes most days on my cross trainer for exercise – it hasn't been difficult – it's been great. It's exactly what I want. Writing this diary and being honest with myself, continually trying to be conscious and aware in the moment is making the difference.

THOUGHT FOR THE DAY
I was talking to a doctor yesterday – we got into
"ultimately, what's your job about?". "Ultimately," he said
"to keep people alive and healthy as long as possible and
ultimately to die well or fit." Is that what it's all about?

22.10.2005   Day 30

Yesterdays thought for the day stayed with me a while. It seems so cold and final – you live then die. I don't believe it's the end.

I believe our body dies but the essence of who we are – our spirit lives on. Energy can not disappear – it becomes transformed into something else – what happens to our spirit I and I guess no-one knows. My mothers' and sisters' spirit I still sense. I think that it's to do with the great love we had between us – every time I see a magpie, I think of my sister Veronica. In her last week of life, we stood together in the kitchen – she took hold of my hand and said "look, that's me when I die – big, cheeky, mischievous and noticeable" – she was pointing to a magpie on the front lawn. I was so lucky and honoured to have the opportunity to talk about dying with my sister before she left us. My mum, well I see her photo every morning and quiet times in the countryside, she walks with me for a while.

One morning, whilst I was doing my exercise and I had some reflective music on – I think it was Enya – I closed my eyes and such a powerful image of all my dead relatives sat together facing me came to mind – I said hello to them all – it was a wonderful feeling. There are many more moments and incidents that tell me there is more after bodily death. I also believe that the quality of this 'after life' is dependant on how you spend 'earth life'. I don't mean if you're bad you go to hell and good go to heaven – more – the more you are alive in every sense on earth, the more your spirit will be experienced, visible – the impact you had on earth will continue long after you have died – in a positive sense. How do I want to be known after I die? I want my life to be balanced with giving and receiving, the latter more difficult for me, but I keep trying. An interesting, some would say morbid, self challenge is to imagine yourself looking at your own gravestone – what would you want it to say? For me, mmm, well – at the moment, something like:

'He made a difference,
A wise contributor,
Selfless and loving,
A wonderful husband,
father, step-father, granddad
and brother.
'Your spirit is alive and well'

What's all this got to do with Fatmea? It's about facing your own mortality, the life you have left, and choosing how you want to spend it. We are all vulnerable and powerful at the same time. Each one of us can make a difference!

WID! Lost 4lbs. Not bad. Now weigh 231lbs. It's going to be a tough week, running conferences, workshops away from home, dinner and drinks with clients. Fatmea thrives on these occasions – a good test – we'll see.

> **THOUGHT FOR THE DAY**
> **The beginning and end are important but the moment in the middle is priceless.**
> **(1 month gone – loss of 14lbs – time to re-read the diary. Sometimes it's good to review insights and learning – they are more likely to stay with you that way.)**

23.10.2005   Day 31

Nearer 60,000 killed in the Pakistan earthquake, hurricane Wilma has just thrashed Mexico and is on its way to Florida, more of our American and British boys have been killed in Iraq, the sun is just rising, birds are singing, I can hear the first traffic of the day – it's difficult to imagine tragedy, chaos and beauty wrapped into one world. It's going on around us and we are all part of it. Some people choose to detach themselves, they avoid the news, don't read newspapers. Others struggle with their daily lives making it difficult to look up and out. I wake and wonder, what surprise will happen today? What ripple of change is happening in the world today? What can I take notice of, what part will I take in the unfolding mystery of life?

I must be one of the luckiest people alive to have a wife that adores me, children that love me and a job that I feel passionate about and enjoy. The only thing that could put this at risk is my physical health and sanity. Physically – well – Fatmea at the moment is under control – sanity – mmmm! What is sanity?

Sanity is based on some idea or concept of what 'normal' is. In the early 1970's, I worked in a large institution with nearly 1000 patients. Mostly locked wards and grounds secured. These institutions no longer exist in the UK. So what's happened? Mental illness reducing? I suspect not. Better treatment, more tolerance, wider definition of what's normal – I suspect all of these and I know that the institution itself caused 'norms of behaviour' that it made it difficult for patients to survive outside.

What's normal to some can be quite abnormal to others – everyone perceives the world differently and who are we to judge what is right or wrong? A guiding principle is to intervene if the person is a danger to others or themselves. At some level in society, we have to judge. Smoking and binge drinking is dangerous to those who indulge and those around. Obesity is dangerous to self. In mental health terms we would intervene, but you can not impose control over other peoples' choices about health – you can do everything possible to make them aware of the consequences of their choice.

As an obese person, I have been deluded, ie a false belief. It is quite insidious. One day, I am 13 stone, another 14 stone – still look OK – trousers a little tight – need another pair anyway – get a size bigger, next thing, I am 15 stone – still feel good, feel fine, no one says anything. 16 stone – some comments, but more to do with how well I look (what they probably mean is 'haven't you put weight on?') 17 stone – OK – overweight, I do feel a little uncomfortable, I'll get round to losing it soon. 17½ stone (245 lbs) – enough is enough – but no-one has said anything.

You get used to being big. Somehow, your fat is OK. You don't look too long at it and get quite ingenious at covering it up – but it's a delusion – you genuinely believe that you are OK and happy. It can't be!! How can anyone be happy dying early with a painful death? I've heard some people say "I am going to live life to the full, then go out with a bang – suddenly!" Nonsense, you can't over indulge and hope to have a heart attack and die – chances are you will have a stroke and live on for years disabled! There are others who say it's good to be fat, leave us alone, it's discrimination, we are happy being large. I don't believe it! I am sure they are convinced, but that's the nature of delusions – given a choice, wouldn't everyone want to be healthy?

Some would say the price is too high. Giving up drinking, smoking, eating all the things associated with pleasure. I say these are 'smoke screens' – they mask real pleasure – look deeper – it's amazing what's there.

So, are fat people insane – no of course not – we just see ourselves and the world differently. If we were insane, we would have no insight – obese people are experts in knowing what they should be doing – what's missing?

Courage and personal belief that they can take charge of their lives and seek greater satisfaction in living through a journey of self discovery.

THOUGHT FOR THE DAY
What am I doing to help my brothers and sisters in Pakistan?
Ask those closest to you – are you concerned for me because I am overweight – honest answer please!!

24.10.2005   Day 32

O God, still this fiery pain inside, give me peace
Controlled desire waiting to unleash
Love sweet and rich like honey wine
To pour over your wounds and quench your thirst
I love you now and even though our love must be cursed
You belong in my heart
I belong in your arms
I'll protect you inside from all the lies, kiss your feet
Your side, your palms, wipe the sweat from your eyes
Don't cry
I have nothing now without you but you're in my heart to stay
You'll come back, don't leave it too long to realise, I pray

Written by Veronica, my sister, age 25, a few weeks before she died.

Help me to receive and to be open
Help me to heal
I lay here willing myself to live
To see, to hear, to feel
Everything I experience, to give fully
My commitment to living
Each day with knowing my vulnerable self
Give me strength to listen and respect myself
In order to contact the healing part
of me that finds health and peace

Written by me whilst recovering from radiotherapy.

Today I am running a workshop for 30 health professionals who want to create a better health service / system for all children across the North West of England.

> ### *THOUGHT FOR THE DAY*
> ### *How can I add value, make a difference and contribute to others well being in a way that contributes to my own?*

25.10.2005   Day 33

Did 5½ hours driving yesterday! Mostly motorways in dangerous conditions. Very wet, lots of spray, visibility poor. Occasionally, some crazy driver – usually a white van or young person makes a suicidal move – for some reason, I was more aware than usual of how risky this was. At any second, my life could be over!

The UK is gridlocked – there are too many cars or too few roads. Something will have to be done soon!

A journey that should have taken two hours took 3½. Usually, I get frustrated and tend to go faster. This time, I concentrated more, relaxed, and stayed within the speed limit. The phrase 'never mind the destination, enjoy the journey' kept coming into mind.

I believe a journey of personal change involves all aspects of life, behaviour and relationships. So, losing weight is one aspect – possibly a catalyst for changing other aspect of life. Your outlook, hopes, dreams, opportunities, confidence, relationships are all mixed up in this recipe for change.

Today I am running a management development workshop – the theme is leadership.

The guys are the senior team in a manufacturing business. The title of the workshop is Change, Challenge and Lead.

I think they will realise that to become an effective leader, they need to understand what their personal power is and what the associated impact and responsibility really means. Welcome to conscious incompetence guys!! Should be a fun day!

Arrived late last night and quite tired – the team were waiting to have a drink and a meal with me. Previously, I would have drunk a couple of pints quickly and had two, possibly three, glasses of wine and a large meal.

Well, I'm quite pleased with myself. I was so conscious of the pint, it was my first for a few weeks – it lasted most of the meal and I could feel its effect. I was aware of every mouthful that went into myself – ate less. It was no big deal – felt good. Get your mind right and this stuff is easy!

THOUGHT FOR THE DAY
'Never mind the destination, enjoy the journey'
'Stop and smell the flowers occasionally'

26.10.2005   Day 34

That was a long day – 10 hours on my feet facilitating this team to help them see the world and themselves differently. Looking at them at the end of the day, I think they were more tired than I – but yes – some of the concepts and feedback went deep and should stick – finish early today so the drive home won't be too bad.

Not sure Fatmea is getting any smaller this week so far. Certainly no bigger, I have been very careful. Being away from home makes it a little more difficult and not got the same opportunity to exercise when I am at work – so – will probably do a little more tomorrow.

It's so easy, when you are busy and really paying attention to others, to forget yourself. The times I am most effective is where I get the balance right between others and self and my observations and input then seem to be more timely and relevant. A lot of my work is to a timetable, it has a flow and session link – so I have to move the group on – I know, however, if I paused a little longer – gave them a little more room to consolidate and talk to each other – the lesson may go deeper and be more effective.

It's doing this and completing the whole programme so they get a sense of what we are trying to achieve. A bit like this diary really – if I pause long enough on an issue about losing weight – it will go deeper – and the journey to self discovery takes another level. I also have to keep reminding myself what this is all about, the bigger picture – longer, healthier life, being happy, create happiness.

At some point, I will need to address the questions: why am I working, travelling on dangerous roads, risking life and limb – for what? To earn a living – what living do I need?

THOUGHT FOR THE DAY
Do I work to live, or live to work? How much do I really
need?

27.10.2005   Day 35

Driving back home yesterday I heard a story on the radio that brought a tear to the eye. A song has just been released, written by a mother for her daughter.

The mum has just been diagnosed with breast cancer for the second time and has been given 6 months to live. She wrote this song and it's been released.

They were both on the radio – mum and the sixteen year old daughter talking about how they are best friends, how much they love each other, how much they share. The song is basically the mum asking her daughter to remember the times they laughed together and the final lines are something like 'if things don't turn out as planned I give to you and place you in your fathers hand'.

I am so special to be witnessing this special type of relationship between mother and daughter in my own family, ie: my wife and my step-daughter – they are so close, phoning everyday, shopping together, going to the theatre – it's good to see – my step-daughter is 21 and an inspiration to me as she has blossomed into a wonderful woman (and lost 3 stone over this last year) and it's going to be exciting sharing her journey through life because I believe she will make a difference.

Another good reason to keep fit and healthy – so we can see the story of our children unfold.

Today, I am attending a 10th Year Celebration of our local carers centre. The network of people who support those who spend most of their time caring for their loved ones at home. This is a particular honour for me as I remember my carer days about 25 years ago when I cared for my baby sister Veronica who was on kidney dialysis on and off for about six years (in between transplants).

We had a machine in a portable building in the back garden. She was on the machine for 4 hours, 3 times a week. In those days, the 'false' kidney had to be built and cleaned afterwards. The whole process took about 8 hours.

I can still see her now – she always made an effort to look good, and sat up in bed keeping cheerful despite the tubes coming out of her arm, having her blood pumped through a couple of plastic boards and cellophane and back again!

The bond between us was great and I still miss her today. She died in my arms on 31st January 1985. My step-daughter was born on 1st February 1984.

When I was training to be a nurse, I worked on a general surgical ward for a time. I remember a particularly distressing case of a young police officer admitted with smashed legs, due to his own colleagues in a car chase involved in apprehending a suspect – they ran into him. One of his legs had to be amputated. He suffered severely from 'phantom pains' screaming out. I had to help occasionally change his dressing on his leg. His career was over. This was 1978.

Now, all these years later, he is immobile and confused and he needs 24 hour care, which is given mainly by two people in his home; his daughter and my step-daughter! (Working part time as a care assistant whilst at University)

It just amazes me how our lives are entwined, the coincidences that occur in life – the meaning of it all. I just think there can be no greater goal than to find out who you are, what you are about and how you relate to this world.

This journey gives you meaning, surprise, delight and excitement because you begin to be alerted by the many beautiful things happening around you every moment of every day.

I also think it increases the opportunities for really connecting with others, form a bond of love and sharing in the celebration of who you are.

THOUGHT FOR THE DAY
Lose weight, find yourself and discover who you are connected to in this world.

28.10.2005   Day 36

I believe one of the ingredients of happiness is in companionship with someone you love and who loves you. I am so fortunate to have found my love. Mave is my second wife and is an amazing woman. Unfortunately, the journey of finding each other was preceded by my divorce from my first wife. This was, as most divorces are, a painful process. I wrote this at the time:

The pain of letting go
Sadness soars its pitiful lament
Who said go with the flow?
Good intentions well meant

The hope of a better future
Lightness beckons its thrill
It will take more than a suture
To cure this heart of ill

What pulls me away is strong
The inner search for meaning
The love that has been lost so long
Or is it me just seething

The anger of knowing what might have been
The tears of joy I have missed
I can not help it but seeing
me held, caressed and kissed

To rescue this tender love of mine
Requires an acceptance of me as me
Not as a pathetic lying swine
But as a good man who is free

Leaving my first wife was difficult – she was a good woman, we just grew apart. We were making each other depressed, our lives were becoming stale – I had to get out before we both drowned.

Now, she is very happy with her new husband and I with my wife – now for 6 years. It takes courage to face up to what's real, and for nearly 20 years, I desperately tried to make my first marriage work. In life's journey we change so much and unless you learn to change together and continue to learn about each other, then separation in some form is inevitable.

Divorce is like a bereavement, only the ex-partner is still alive – and when on occasion you see each other again, it's like a visit from a ghost, a blast from the past – unless of course you create some new relationship between you. It's another example of something I must let go of – pain was unavoidable – there is no easy way to divorce, but it has now passed and we are both happy.

So, the journey through life is enriched if shared with a loved one. My father-in-law, who is 83, is now on his own – my mother in law died 6 years ago. He has a sort of shrine on a table at home with pictures and candles. Her room and clothes have not been touched, there are still two places set for dinner although he has not eaten in there since her death and he has never missed a Sunday morning visit to the cemetery. For him, his companion is her image and her memory – he cannot let go and he is very much alone in his grief.

Grief has been a significant part of my make-up over the years and I have worked very hard at expressing my anger and tears – however, I – at times – still run my fingers over the scars of loss.

THOUGHT FOR THE DAY
To lighten up – you have to let go!

29.10.2005   Day 37

The wind on your face, the smell of fresh air, the sound of the trees and the trickle of water from a fall, the bleat of sheep and the chatter of friends around you. The feeling of warmth and the sensation of breathing harder with your heart pumping more and more as you climb. The beauty of the scenery and the majestic roll of the hills; with the different shades of green, against a background of cloud variations continually changing and a rainbow in the distance. The anticipation of what's over the hill or around the next cliff all add up to a great walking weekend with friends.

If I was any heavier, I would struggle to keep up – my friends are, on average, about six years older than I, but fitter. It must be awful for those who are home or chair bound because of illness, even worse if it's through obesity! Another benefit of losing weight is to be lighter – so the legs don't have to work as hard and the opportunities increase to explore this wonderful world of ours.

WID! Loss of another 4 lbs! Now 227lbs, I am pleased with that given my schedule and the overindulgence occasionally with the wine! My formulae seems to be working so far and it's no hardship – light breakfast, fruit for lunch or a salad, then a good meal in the evening. Cut down on potatoes, bread, cheese, pasta and increase fruit and veg. Very moderate on the booze and no snacks. It's working so far and I am eating what I want, just less of it!

THOUGHT FOR THE DAY
Go to your nearest countryside – drink in the scenery, its beauty is almost a match for the beauty inside of us!

30.10.2005   Day 38

100 people blown up and killed, many more injured in Delhi, 3 million homeless in Pakistan about to a face a murderous winter,

the president of Iran states that Israel should be 'wiped out' yet the autumn sun still glistens and dances on the orange and red leaves, the wind blows and the laughter shrills into the night.

I felt good yesterday – filled my lungs with air and sang at the top of my voice disturbing the peace and quiet of the countryside. Then ran down the hill – what a thrill – all spontaneous – why?? It's good to be aware of yourself and conscious all the time, but if it's too concentrated then it can become too intense, controlled – where's the fun, where's the spontaneity? I think its good to loosen up from time to time – laugh out loud, keep laughing – we are all too serious – lighten up!

THOUGHT FOR THE DAY
Lose the weight, cry less, laugh more!

31.10.2005   Day 39

A recent survey of British employers illustrated that a significant majority would choose a thin person rather than a fat person.

The prejudice and stereotypes related to being fat are often unspoken, apart from the kids that get bullied at school and the comedian or presenters who flaunt it as part of their act.

A friend of ours will always stare and make a comment at someone who is obese – the comment relates to a judgement, a criticism – something like – that's gross, disgusting, causing us taxpayers a lot of money through bad health, why haven't these people got willpower. He is, I believe, projecting his own fears on to others – he is obsessed with his own health and not the most relaxed person in the world.

Those who judge others say a lot about themselves and yes – I would dearly love everyone to be healthy and happy – but if someone chooses to be overweight, smokes and drinks to excess – that's their choice – it doesn't make them a bad person. Everyone chooses within their own level of awareness and development.

I am the sort of person, if anyone, who deserves to be judged or criticised – because I know the theory, I have the awareness yet I still struggle.

Judging others is also a way of feeling 'good' about yourself. In a way – it's feeding your 'ego' – this image we portray that conveys status, power, control, possessions, achievements – they're all our mask – not truly who we are, but what we represent to the outside world.

By comparing yourself to others (which is what essentially judgement is) we feed this image.

I love the story in the Bible where Jesus stops a stone throwing of a woman accused of adultery by saying those without a blemish, a stain or who has not sinned may throw the first stone – of course, no one did. We all have our misdemeanours and have made mistakes – if we dig deep enough into anyone's past – a dark shadow could be found – it's human to trip and fall and thank God it is also human to learn and move on.

THOUGHT FOR THE DAY
Forgive others, forgive ourselves, give everyone a chance to live and hope for a better future.

01.11.2005   Day 40

Witches, goblins, vampires, scream masks, Frankenstein, Shrek, ghosts and headless monsters were just some of our visitors last night. Trick or treat seems to have got more popular over here in the UK recently – we gave out 80 packets of sweets!

It's great to see the youngsters dress up and I hope one message of Halloween is not lost – that is – it's good to laugh at those things we invent ourselves to scare us! I remember as a child that my two younger sisters and I used to take delight in seeing who could scare the other the most. Even today we can joke about it. My imagination as a child was vivid. I remember having my own guardian angel whom I often talked to. I remember having a little army of men who used to go into battle with me. I remember a nightmare that kept repeating where the sky turned green, voices from the sky told me to go home as my family was in danger – as I go into the hall – hands come from behind the clothes horse and grab me – I fight – I wake – gasping for breath.

The scariest TV programme I watched was the Outer Limits. I watched it sitting close to mum and behind a cushion - going to bed afterwards - all the lights had to be on - and I had to whistle up the stairs! Even today, the hairs on the back of my neck stand up, my skin comes alive when I detect something close to me that I don't quite understand. Early childhood experiences can stay with you for life - for me - I am fortunate as I believe my mum did a great job - my father hardly there. I wonder what my children will remember? I had a text from one of my sons yesterday "sat with Oliver on my knee watching the dolphin show" - they have taken my grandson on his first holiday abroad. I replied "treasure these precious moments". I can remember taking my sons for the first time to see the greatest show on earth - Shamu - the Killer Whale at Sea World, Florida. The first time I saw this show, I cried at the beauty, majesty and the miracle before my eyes. One of the most powerful creatures on earth playing with the most dangerous creature on earth (man).

My boy's faces were a picture - and of course - they had to get splashed. I do miss them as young boys - as teenagers, they were a challenge - now, as young men, they are coming back slowly. I wrote this and sent it to them when they were in teenage turmoil (through the period of my divorce)

Dreaming last night
Gave me a wondrous sight
Playing with my boys
No toys, but noise
Of laugher, fun and tumbles
Yet the vision fades and crumbles
Both hold on so small
Their dad looking so tall
Oh how times have changed

My boys are now young men
No longer bright eyed and 10
They enjoy their drink
Take life to the brink
Visit their old man now and then

They have seen their dad in all his glory
Sad and lonely, not the tall hero he was
It's no fairy tale now, more of a war story
Where two who were one are sorry
But now see how each can live more fully
Oh how times have changed

I miss you boys, you were my best friends
I love you dearly
I want you to be happy, healthy and safe
Take care
Visit your old man now and then
I can still walk tall

love Dad.

It's natural for us to want our children to be proud of us as it is for parents to be proud of our children. Whether we like it or not, as parents we are powerful role models and the chances that our kids will repeat some of the patterns we created in their early life are great.

So, if we live our life around TV and major on a diet of fast food – chances are our children will grow up to do the same. I want my children to have a lasting image of their dad being fit and healthy, one who took a pride in good but healthy living.

I don't want them to have negative images of their parents, like myself for example – I have my mum in a coma, rigid, fed on a tube and my father, lonely, overweight, sat in his small flat watching TV with a glass of whisky.

I want them to remember me as a marathon runner, a golfer, a rugby referee, laughing, travelling the world and above all – a loving, doting father. We can not control out children's behaviour but we can do our best to show them what works in life.

This is our choice – and that requires keeping fit!

THOUGHT FOR THE DAY
It's never too late to give the message it's OK to choose the direction that leads to home, where you are safe, accepted and loved.

What lasting image do you want your children and family to have of you?

02.11.2005   Day 41

God is greater than psychology
So I think I owe myself an apology
I've been living in sin
Trapped in my darkness within
But now I am free
I can truly see
That Heaven is here and hell is there
And there is not much more between
God, that word blurted out in condemnation
God, the word that clues us in to the nature of creation
Who or what and where is God?
Stop looking, he or she is here, it's you
David Ike – on your bike, hang him from a tree
How can God resemble someone like me

A liar, a cheat, selfish and sullen
Is this the figure of being I worship
Or do my feelings of grief betray me
Can it be that God is simpler than this
Can it be the God is me and you are God
Therefore Jesus was man

Jesus had a terrific philosophy and the power to heal.
Is there a Jesus alive today?

We all have the potential to heal and live by and create a Christian philosophy. So, what after death, the soul, the spirit, it lives – in what form – the ghosts, the sightings, the near death experiences, the connection with those deceased – can these be our desperate attempts to hang on and communicate with our loved ones, does the body change to higher planes of existence – does not knowing or not having tangible proof have to stop us believing? Can we have faith?

The prayer, the church, the symbols, the Bible are ways of helping us to compete against everything material.

These things, including many addictions we have, stack up against God being known, because it's difficult to be still – to hear what's real, what is me, what is God, it is a shame that many only find God and peace near death – the joy of God can be found on the journey of discovering who you really are.

Losing weight, achieving long lasting and sustainable health I believe is a Spiritual journey. It requires discipline, daily reflection or meditation and deep love for your fellow human being.

The questions I have about my religion are all healthy because they help me to discover new things about myself and others – they keep my feet on the ground and remind me that no one is better than anyone else – we are from the same source and part of the same family.

Losing the first 14lbs in weight is easy – now we have to focus and continue to believe in what I want to achieve – determined for the outcome and to enjoy and learn whilst on the journey.

THOUGHT FOR THE DAY
In what ways can you connect with your God today? How can God help me lose weight? What prayer makes sense?

03.11.2005   Day 42

You know there is no getting away from it. If you put in more than you put out then you increase in weight. The excess energy is stored as fat!!

Love your body, love its movement, dance, walk, run, exercise – do anything to get the heart beating. This will, in turn, burn off the calories, increase your metabolism and make your body more efficient.

Exercise also produces endorphins – these are hormones in the brain that give you a feeling of well being – a lift, a buzz – who needs drugs!!

Unfortunately my sister did. She was a heroin addict, which, in the end, significantly contributed to her death. Through using dirty needles, she caught Hepatitis which made her very infective, so any dialysis on a kidney machine had to be done in a specially protected environment. Also, with her abuse of her injection sites, it became difficult to attach dialysis needles, and eventually her access arm (called a shunt) deteriorated. It was at this point that one of my regrets in life emerges.

Apparently, Veronica – my sister – decided enough was enough. She didn't want an operation to help her have further dialysis – she wanted to die in peace. The doctors explained the difficulty – operating on Veronica is dangerous to staff because she has Hepatitis and given her track record of drug addiction, her chance of a further transplant is slim.

The doctors accepted Veronica's decision – I did not, until Veronica herself requested it to me direct. I still feel today – if I had fought it, she may still be alive. I was not strong enough at the time.

Today there are units that specialise in dialysing patients with Hepatitis. But Veronica and the family were supportive – and I was alone and weak. Something else I have to forgive myself for. I'll tell you more of her story later, but for now, she also kept diaries. Shortly after her death, as I was reading them, I discovered the following:-

My brother I love you
I owe you so much
You helped me escape from deaths ugly clutch
You gave me strength when illness was pain
You made me laugh and helped keep me sane
You comforted me when our mother was gone
You showed me good where I thought there was none
You set me free to go my own way
Ever watchful, you knew I would stray
But again you were there to comfort me
When at last from the clutches of death I broke free
You tried to warn me I wouldn't hear
I learn from my own mistakes, I fear
But now when I find my spirit is free
Please don't doubt me, let me be me
I feel I've maybe come further than you
I see and feel and know what to do

So please, keep loving and worry no more
I know myself now, down to the core
The path I choose now will be strong, straight and true
But remember brother, I'll always love you

Veronica, born 23.12.1960, died 31.01.1985

What a wonderful gift she has given me – it was and still is a painful letting go process, even after all these years. I still sense her presence, I must let her go.

So, where was I? Oh yes – so who needs drugs? Who needs addictions? Addictions are those things that become habitual and eventually we become dependant. Drugs, alcohol and smoking are obvious examples – but could we view our eating habits as an addiction? Mmmm – I wonder …

> ### *THOUGHT FOR THE DAY*
> ***If only … this is wasted emotion as we do what we do at the time with best intentions and within our own limited awareness.***

04.11.2005   Day 43

Have you noticed that when you start to lose weight people start to comment – "Have you lost weight?", "you're looking good". It now becomes discussable. You very rarely get 'haven't you put weight on' or 'you're looking really unhealthy'. Maybe if more people did say what they thought – more people would be encouraged to take an honest look at themselves. My advice to myself is to play it down – don't make a big deal of it – you're not losing weight for others – it's for you and you have a long way to go yet.

Even though I have lost over a stone in weight, a peculiar phenomenon happens – I become even more conscious of my fat. I look fatter. I feel fatter. This is OK – it's healthy because now I am registering a truer picture of myself, whereas before I was in denial.

I'll be surprised if I lose more than 2lbs this week. Although I have been eating healthily, ie nothing fried, no potatoes or bread, no snacks or booze, minimum cheese and pasta – I have been eating loads of fruit and vegetables and salad. This is all good roughage but still calories – I suspect my portions have been on the large size.

I could get into calorie counting which I have done before and I know roughly what is high in calories and what is not. Some people may be surprised by the calorie content of some food. It may be worth adding them up sometime to get an idea of what level of intake we should be having. For me to lose weight – I should have less than 2000 calories a day – combine this with a daily 20 minute aerobic exercise and a steady weight loss will be achieved. I don't feel calorie controlled diets work, but it's useful and sensible to know which foods are very high so I have listed the obvious ones at the back of this book.

I read recently in a newspaper someone claiming that if you are poor and of a poor education you are prone to obesity because you don't know better and have less access to healthy nutritious food. I find that difficult to believe because of the massive education and media message about the dangers of obesity and the importance of eating healthily, also – if you are poor and obese then I assume they have been able to afford more food than you need, spent money on the wrong food – I suspect not because it was cheaper, but because it was easier to get to. I think the fast food chains are offering more healthier options but much more needs to be done to offer an alternative to fried chicken, burger, chips and pizzas. We need more accessible and appetizing options and choices.

Keeping the momentum going in this battle of the bulge is important. Fatmea still wins from time to time – ie, I keep eating even though I am full!

It's important to remind myself, every time I eat:

1 Why am I eating? Do I need this?
2 What I want – my vision of golf for next 30 years, pain free joints and to Disney with my Grandchildren.
3 Be alive to what's happening around me – drink and eat this life experience and the need for food becomes less.

THOUGHT FOR THE DAY 1
An inch closer to your goal is better than losing sight of it. Never give up!

I have, particularly since my cancer, gone through a phase of fear. Fear causes anxiety and depression which can result in a lack of care for self which then results in eating and drinking to excess.

Unresolved grief can also be a factor contributing to anxiety and depression.

So facing your grief and fears are important aspects of knowing yourself. Also, having a little knowledge can be worse than ignorance as this knowledge contributes to anxiety and fear. So, what are my fears?

Dying young with cancer.

Being disabled with Multiple Sclerosis (my aunty died of MS - she was a beautiful opera singer with the Doyle Carte company) also, I have had problems with my balance - a virus the doctors say, and my bladder - muscle problems and a retentive bladder.

Fear of my children coming to harm, not being happy or dying before me.

Fear of my wife dying before me.

Fear is a destructive and disabling emotion, and as I write this I realise how little they come into play in my life. It's all fear of loss in some shape or form, but if you think about it, as each moment passes - it's gone - lost, we move on.

The more I focus on fear of things that might never happen, the less chance I have of realising and enjoying the moment.

I also think the more you focus on fears and negative possibilities, the chances are they will happen.

As a child, I remember dreaming about mum and dad dying and being left alone - as a result in my dreams, I got a lot of attention and sympathy. Mum did die young, dad was always away - there was no extra attention or sympathy. There is something powerful that goes on in this world of ours - it's called a 'self fulfilling prophecy' - if you think hard enough, believe deep enough that something will happen - it will.

We must harness these phenomena in a positive way - rid ourselves of all negative thoughts and fears and think positively about ours and others lives.

Self determination, goal and vision achievement based on regular and continuous affirmation of the love for humanity. Believe that we can all achieve a better life – start with ourselves – lose the fear. Fear can lead to hatred especially if it's linked to threat – when it gets to this stage it becomes physically destructive. We must not give in to fear. Love and celebrate the moment.

THOUGHT FOR THE DAY 2
The more you are aware of what is happening now, the less concerned you are about what comes next.

05.11.2005   Day 44

It's official! The most important factor to determine the chances of having a heart attack is not your weight or your body mass index – it's the size of your belly!

Beer belly men, are you prepared for this? Published in this months' British Medical Journal are the results of research where thousands of heart attack victims were measured.

Conclusive results show that if your waist is bigger than your hips, then you have a three times greater chance of having a heart attack.

This is because of the type of fat laid down around the abdomen releases chemicals that interfere with the insulin release mechanism which in turn increases the likelihood of overeating and diabetes.

So, what's mine – well they say for men it should be 0.9, ie the figure after you have divided your hip measurement into your waist measurement (for women it is 0.85), So, my hip size is 44", my waist size is 46" which equals 1.05.

The problem here is, of course, as I lose weight, my hip size reduces also – so I just hope my belly fat goes quicker than my hip fat!

And another thing! The world health organisation can not back up with evidence that the recommended intake of 5 portions of fruit and veg a day makes up a healthy diet. In fact, most research and dieticians are saying that that's the minimum and it should be between seven and ten portions.

God help America then – cos I see them eating less fruit and veg than us in the UK.

I manage most days a couple of pieces of fruit, some salad and two or three veg in the evening with my meal. But I bet most people struggle to eat this. In which case – it's a contributor to obesity. Because if you're not eating veg or fruit, you're probably eating fat instead and of course bowel cancer occurs more where meat and fat is a dominant feature of the diet.

WID – 225lbs – loss of only 2lbs this week. That's OK – I know I have slipped a few times – occasional glass of wine, a few snacks, a heavy weekend with friends last weekend. But hey – still in the right direction and no real hardship.

Back to waist/hip ratio – I have also read that a man's waist should not be over 40" – therefore I have to lose 6" off my waist and 4" off my hips to get anywhere near the ideal ratio.

I've lost 20lbs, another 30 to go! This would take me just below 14 stone – what I think is realistic and then we will review the situation then! So, if I want to avoid being one of the 300,000 people a year in Britain who have a heart attack, I better get working on Fatmea – you're still going my fat friend and by the way – you're smaller now and I am in a stronger position to deal with you!

THOUGHT FOR THE DAY
It's all about balance, proportion and awareness.

06.11.2005   Day 45

Bangs, flashes, thunder, wheezes, whistles, crackles and screeches – yep! It's that time of year again! We live in a village square and so any noise around us is reverberated and is exaggerated, so when the fireworks go up, which they do almost at the back of every home, we are in what seems to be like the middle of a war zone. Between 5.30 and 10.30, the night is bombarded with gunpowder explosions – the sky is lit up and slowly, the evening is filled with smoke.

It's another one of those traditions I remember as a child – going round to my Aunties, eating home made toffee, toffee apples, jacket potato with butter and salt, sausages – my own sparkler in hand

and what a great night ! Celebrating Guy Fawkes – the man born and educated here in York – yet all over England on 5th November – his effigy is burnt on a bonfire, just because he failed to blow up British Parliament 400 years ago!

My son told me he is getting married! He has been living with a divorcee with two young children for six months. He has bought a £1,000 pedigree French Mastif – a dog and a half! He now wants to settle down. He is 27 and now has an instant family! They are getting married in 6 months time. Someone once said – as parents, we craft and shape the wood for the bow, we ensure the tension of the string is right at the time we pull back and take our children as the arrow. Point straight and true in the right direction – and then let go! Well, I think I have done this to my best ability, however, I think the arrow will hit various things on its way, maybe deflected off its path from time to time – but I believe its made of strong stuff, got a great start and will eventually hit its target!

I just hope my sons learn and make their decisions about life partners with a full and intense belief, as I did when I committed to their mother, and as I have committed to my wife.

I just hope the experience they have witnessed somehow has given them an impression that marriage isn't some phase you go through, then it changes and you go through it again with someone else.

When you get married, you must do so with a deep intense belief and love that this is for life and it is exactly what you want. Well, I guess I've given them that message – perhaps my credibility in giving them it is a little tainted. Just like my credibility about keeping fit and healthy – I tell them it's important – but they haven't got a good role model yet.

That will change.

Having children is one of the most selfless things in life to do. You give so much and dedicate so much time and emotion.

My world revolved around my children – and the door will always be open for my sons and my step-children. I wish I had had more children but my wife didn't want to. She was shocked at having twins in the first place and said she was going to have a hysterectomy. I couldn't let her do that – it was a major operation – it was easier for me to get the snip.

So, I had a vasectomy at the age of 25, in a private clinic, back streets of Bradford – it was awful – afterwards, I got an infection – epididymitis – the worst pain I have experienced in my life. I am convinced today that the seeds of testicular cancer started there. At the time, there was no counselling or anything – the doctor said OK – are you sure – fine – go here!

I have always regretted it – I would have liked more children and ideally a child with my second wife, however, age was against us. But hey – another if only.... another regret – in the past, let it go. Celebrate the children we have – I'm a lucky man!

THOUGHT FOR THE DAY
We do our best at the time, hope and pray they love and shine.

07.11.2005   Day 46

11th night of riots in France – 1000's of cars burnt, two youths killed – is this the new French Revolution? Power response – they will be caught and punished – wrong! The politicians need to walk the streets – listen to the young people, appeal to community leaders – something has gone dreadfully wrong! French policy of integrating cultures, supporting the young, the poor and the immigrant population is not working. If you deal with violence with violence, you get more violence – I believe the elected body have a responsibility to listen and act – not act then listen.

I'm still eating too much – you have to be honest with yourself in this journey. The sense in my stomach triggers off an urge to eat to satisfy it – I then visualise what that might be – I have difficulty ignoring it until I eat what I want. So I think the key here is to retrain the message from my stomach – if it says hungry – say no. Drink water, wait. Remind self of goal. Do something to focus away from food.

Also, portions are still on the big side and I caught myself eating quickly while watching TV last night – so again, time to remind myself of the basics I have already highlighted in this diary. I feel the need to restate my prayer –

Help me to be
This moment is as it should be
Conscious choice in every moment
Breathe and recognise my connection with
Everything around me and the fact that it
Is I that is creating this moment.

Be uplifting, loving and give to my
Fellow humans, explore coincidences – follow through.
Seek opportunities to help others,
Eat and drink less, meditate and pray
Be in touch with my body
Judge and control less, go with the flow
Trust the positive energy I am creating
Be less attached to outcome and more present in the now
Be in touch with my feelings
Listen and value what my heart says – follow through on my
intuition
My world and my relationships are a reflection of me
I am in union with these things
My purpose in life is to know who I am
and in this journey create happiness and fulfilment for me and
others
This requires forgiveness
This requires giving and receiving love freely.

The longer I live, the more chance I have for living out my prayer – the less overweight I am, the happier I will be for the rest of my life. God – give me strength.

THOUGHT FOR THE DAY
There are many reasons why we eat – identify them – then reduce them!

08.11.2005   Day 47

As a young boy, I guess from the age of about 8 to 12, I used to spend hours on the river bank of the River Ouse in York. My grandfather taught me how to fish.

He fought in the 1st World War as a Sergeant in the 11th Hussars Cavalry – I have a picture of him charging with his lance and his certificate of competence of horsemanship.

He went fishing every day to the same spot by the river, at the bottom of where he lived, at the same time, using the same bait – hemp seed.

He used to say – they know we are here and it's a battle between us and them – who is the smarter?

Since those days, I have always had an urge to land the big one! One day I was fishing – caught a small roach then the biggest pike I have ever seen grabbed the roach as I was reeling it in – we fought for a few seconds – it let go. When I pulled the roach in, it had big teeth marks all down its side. I spent years trying to repeat that moment – I never did.

My father took me sea fishing a few times with his pals – we sailed out of Filey and fished with multiple hooks. I remember a day when we must have put down in a shoal of Mackerel – there was about 10 of us in this boat and all had at least 3 hooks using mussels as bait – for about 20 minutes, everyone was puling 3 on each line. I was only about 9 or 10 at the time, but the excitement was intense. One trip, I won 10 shillings for the largest fish – a cod. Nearly as big as me! I mention this because it strikes me that even at a young age I appreciated the quiet moments – time to think and just be myself.

When I first went self employed – I had time on my hands – about 16 years ago, and took out the old fishing rods. There seemed to be less fish in the old River today – so I wrote down my thoughts:

Flies, butterflies and lies
Bobbing float teasing line
Thirsty banks holding on
to the variety of man, time
will tell to gather in the truth

Life of mine, fishing line
Catch a moment and live
in the murky river of drought
who's flow stems from heaven
and seeps to the vast ocean of life

A gasp of air, a painful tug
The glass edge broken
The size, a surprise, a child
with trauma, swims back to heal

The purpose of it all?
All of it purposeful?
Full?
Empty?

THOUGHT FOR THE DAY
What's the big catch? What's out there? Fish in peace.

09.11.2005   Day 48

America has just reiterated that the biggest threat to their nation's health is obesity and they quote a 5 fold increase in type 2 diabetes amongst the young.

We do quite well to deter people from smoking, but generally shy away from pushing the dangers of obesity. It's challenging to face up to and believe that the following are all increased risks for those overweight:

Heart attack
Stroke
Diabetes – poor circulation, loss of limbs, loss of sight
Arthritis – painful limbs
Bowel cancer
Chronic respiratory disease
Chronic heart disease
Depression
Haemorrhoids

Stomach ulcer and cancer

and more ...

If you are obese, you are very likely to die young from some form of the above!

It's amazing how the mind can protect you from difficult messages. This can be good or bad. These pauses or filtered messages are called 'defence mechanisms'. They are designed to give us time to come to terms with something quite confronting or shocking. However, sometimes this defence lasts for life – hence a lifetime of obesity. Defending against the painful truth, the truth of choosing to die young.

Denial is what is going on here. This happens when someone is told their loved one has died – the truth is painful to accept so the mind says no. It can be more subtle than this and happened to me when I was 22 years old.

I had just returned from a day trip. I was a nurse supervising a group of psychiatric patients on a bus from Scarborough. I was accompanied by my new boss – John, who had started working with us the week before. He was keen to get on with us and show us what he was made of. When we were ready to go home, he offered me a lift in his car. The car was a Reliant Robin – a small 3 wheel fibreglass van – I declined as I had my bicycle. He then insisted and said my bike would fit in the van – which it would if we left the door open! So, no. Eventually, he accepted and I saw him speed away ahead of me to the main road and disappear round the corner. 1 minute later I came to the same corner. This was the scene.

A car, which could have been Johns' – it looked the same colour but was unrecognisable – was smashed in pieces in the middle of the road. A large articulated lorry was parked on the opposite side of the road with the driver sat calmly, staring. There were 3 people on the side of the road stood watching, and one person picking up a few pieces of car from the road.

It was quiet and still. First thoughts in my head – could this be John's car? I got off my bike, looked into the car – saw that no-one was there. Then my mind told me this had happened sometime ago – everything was in hand, the person who was driving has got out and is being looked after. The car is similar to John's – but not his. I can't do anything to help. Off I go home.

As I was riding home, I kept thinking – could it be John's car? If so, was he thrown out. Had it just happened? If so, where were the Emergency services? I decided it wasn't John's car.

Tomorrow I went to work – there was a note on the desk. 'John will not be in to work for some time – he is in intensive care having had a serious accident last night'. I then went into shock, felt sick and ashamed. What happened?

Apparently, John was in the car – underneath the engine – I didn't look close enough. A colleague of mine came shortly after I left and was first (not really, because I was) to the scene and offered first aid. What am I – a coward?

I think back to that time – my mind unconsciously told me – it could have been me in the car – I could have died. My mind went into self preservation mode – or I couldn't possibly take in and act on being the person to discover John – who, by anyone's standards should have died. His legs were smashed and he is still today probably walking with difficulty.

Now I am thinking – if I accepted the lift – he may have avoided the lorry and the crash.

Why do things happen – what's the meaning?

All I know from this is the power of the mind to play games with reality. Something might be obvious, in front of your eyes – but somehow you don't see it!

We became quite good friends, John and I, my guilt driving me to visit regularly, we played chess and I supported where I could. Never again will I shy away from trauma. It shows that being conscious in every moment requires you to face what's happening now and question what's real.

Even this you do to your best ability at the time and there are no guarantees of getting it right – as we get older and hopefully wiser – then our mind strengthens and is able to deal with the horrors we face from time to time.

THOUGHT FOR THE DAY
Look hard at what you see – touch it, check out your feelings – ask someone else – get close to what is real.

10.11.2005   Day 49

Had a pint of lager and two glasses of wine last night with my meal. This was with participants on the development programme I was running. A long day, 8am to 6.30pm – on stage – a one man show. I enjoy it because I see the lights going on in these people. Even though the work is in a business context – I know the insights they have will make a difference to their lives. But, boy, was I exhausted? I really was beginning to feel drunk – difficulty stringing my words together, so left early and I was in bed by 10pm. I now rarely drink during the week and when I do, it is usually no more than a pint, or a couple of glasses of wine.

Alcohol is in the same league as food – the more you have, the more you want or think you need.

Some people think there is such a thing as an addictive personality, ie people prone to alcoholism or gambling, or becoming dependant on other substances, food or drugs – I recognise in myself how easy it could be to go back to a bottle of wine a night – sometimes more. Over time, I would eventually become dependent.

I believe my father was what I call a controlled alcoholic. What saved him was, for years, he worked on oil rigs and alcohol was not allowed. However, I know he used to smuggle whiskey on board and have known my mother send him a package, disguised, with whiskey in. But nevertheless, this life style did constrain him – in his retirement however, he was never alone – he always had his drink for company.

My sons, unfortunately, have grown up in the era of 'binge' drinking, ie youths going out on a Friday and Saturday, from the age of 15 – drinking until they collapse! 10 pints of lager and a bottle of spirits would not be unusual. Despite warning messages and lectures from the old man – for years – this was the pattern.

God knows what it has done to their liver. Again, they see their dad as a drinker – this is a macho thing to do. It's not an image I am proud of and I hope I have changed this image.

My boys are now settling down and I think, I hope, I pray they are drinking less!

The UK is a ticking time bomb for alcoholism and liver disease – something must be done soon. It's strange how many of the addictions, apart from gambling, maybe are all about taking in chemicals to alter your mind – even food can come into this bracket. You think you're hungry, you think you want to experience a taste sensation, so you put something in your mouth, or seek out that to satisfy the urge – a burger, pizza, Indian, Chinese, crisps – arrgh!! Just writing it conjures up a food fest! Mind and body are inseparable – it's when we forget this that things go wrong and out of control.

THOUGHT FOR THE DAY
Addiction can be a way of denying who you really are.

11.11.2005   Day 50

Now over 97,000 dead and still rising in Pakistan. 56 dead in bombs in hotels in Jordan last night, more terrorist attacks in Iraq. Tony Blair, our Prime Minister, has just lost a Government battle for the first time over his proposals to give our police and security forces the authority to detain someone for up to 90 days without charge.

I say, if you have no connection with subversive activity, no connection to extremist groups, then you have no fear of this authority.

If the police say they need it to do their job – then so be it. However, strong political games and the civil liberty lobby have won this time round.

My grandfather (on my mother's side) would be turning in his grave! Chief Constable Fred Milburn. As a young policeman, he used to walk the notorious Walmgate and Fossgate areas in York where every third building was a pub, and the majority of the inhabitants were Irish immigrants in the early 1900's. His way was to get in amongst them, know their faces, thump them if he had too, use his truncheon occasionally and gain the respect of the landlords. By all accounts, he did well – becoming the most senior constable in York. I think his methods (apart from thumping perhaps!) are still relevant today – but getting in amongst them and knowing who they are is a bit more complex and tricky these days!

He was a great man, my grandfather, and I was fortunate to know him until I was in my early 20's. I used to visit him regularly and he used to collect stamps for me – quite a collection which I hold with pride today. His second wife – we called her Aunty Hilda – was a well meaning lady, but rarely took air to stop talking, and therefore, I always came away wishing to have more time with Granddad. I visited him in hospital when he was quite ill, had a long chat. I said I must go (I can't remember what for) – he said stay a little longer? I shook his hand and said I will come back tomorrow. I left. He died that night. Never again will I ignore the wishes of someone ill and alone.

WID tomorrow – not confident given the occasional lapse. We'll see.

THOUGHT FOR THE DAY
If we really listen to our loved ones, what can we hear?
11th hour, 11th day, 11th month – I remember and thank you for your sacrifice.

12.11.2005   Day 51

Loss of only 1lb this week. A bit disappointing. The factors? Working away from home, not enough exercise, too many glasses of wine and my vulnerable time – evenings, unwinding, TV and portions of food on the large size. Fatmea does seem smaller though and I can almost grab her with two hands. I think the two stone overweight must be entirely concentrated around my middle. This week, I am not away at all – until Friday when I take my wife to Barcelona for her birthday. We are out tonight with my sons' prospective parents-in-law, meeting them for the first time and then tomorrow night out with friends who want to take us out – again, to celebrate my wife's birthday as they aren't around on the actual date. So, hardly easy sensible eating environment. Normally, I would overindulge on both occasions; thoroughly enjoy myself, food, drink and company. This time – I am going to put the company first, be more aware of the food and the drink of life, be more in touch with my need for nourishment rather than the habit of eating because it's there – forewarned is forearmed. We'll see!

Yesterday was Remembrance Day. Our oldest war veteran laid a wreath at a memorial statue in France – he is 109 years old and fought in the trenches of the First World War. Both my grandfathers fought in the same war, and my father and his brothers in the Second World War. I am the first generation in this Country not to have to be called up. However, in my teens and early 20's – I was very much aware of our young American boys dieing in Vietnam. If I was American, then – no doubt – I would have been of the age to serve my time in the living hell that was the War no one could win.

Now we live with the daily threat of terrorism, every trip on the train or plane, or visit to a popular public place or favourite holiday destination now is a potential target.

Reflecting on the bravery of the young men and women who have already died in too many wars gives me a sense of pride and shame. Pride that people fight to protect their loved ones, shame because we are all capable of killing another fellow human – who are no better or no worse than us. We make them into something less to justify killing them – this is not right. Peace has to be the way for all our sakes.

I don't want to go to war
I want to grow up and love
Someone down to the core
Yet it seems this is the law
And yes, command from above
I will obey, and lay my life,
For what, I know someday, for love
She could be one day my wife.

We go to war on the wave of a cause, to protect our way of life, our freedom, our values, and so does every one else. Who's right?

THOUGHT FOR THE DAY
If only we could acknowledge and realise the potential we have as humans to share and celebrate what we have in common, without fear of losing, without need to protect or control and with a genuine love for life.

13.11.2005   Day 52

Remembrance Sunday – we will never forget those who will never grow old.

I had a great day yesterday, all my children round; Thomas and my grandson to watch England beat Australia at Rugby Union, Philippa with her friend and little daughter, Myles (my step-son) who came to fix a friends' computer and then out with Matthew and his new fiancé Laura last night. Also, watched England beat Argentina at soccer and watched Madonna with Parkinson and the X-Factor! What a lazy but long and entertaining day!

Yet, woke up this morning with a sense of negativism – reflecting on things in the past I regret and couldn't put my finger on why. We are out with friends tonight, then that got me reflecting on the meaning of friendship. Either I have a too idealistic view of what friendship is, or I am very bad at making and keeping friends.

My only close, deep, real friend in life is my wife Mave. At one time, I was very close to GD. We worked, trained together and wrote a book together – but we drifted apart and although we can quickly reconnect when we get together – he doesn't know me really, nor I him.

I suppose I have this sense that a real close friend is a relationship based on love and respect. This I have experienced very few times in my life outside of my family.

I have many people who we get together with, and when we do – enjoy each others' company, show interest in each others lives and would come to our aid and support us if we needed it. And maybe that's it. I think what I am rambling on about – is a real sense of disappointment in the way I connect or don't connect with people. Friends come and go – real friends stay in touch – I and my 'friends' are really bad at that. I give up too early I guess, I write a letter, make a call or email – then if no response, or I don't get it returned – then months, then years pass by before we reconnect, if we ever do. (Maybe it's a man thing).

This feeds my cynicism about friendship – if they really cared – they would call – if I really cared I would chase! Who needs friends anyway?! Have you also noticed that all my friends are men and all my wife's friends are women – I think this is because it is rare to have a friend of the opposite sex where some attraction or sexual chemistry does not exist, therefore it could be seen as a threat to an existing relationship – therefore better avoided. This all sounds very limiting – and not the ideal free loving, learning, sharing image of my self I would like – however, it's honest and realistic.

What need am I satisfying in this cry for friendship? My quest is to see if I am worth loving – given who I am – given someone really knowing me – can they still love me? Why do I need this? It's part of my quest for knowing who I am, loving who I am, accepting me for me. I know I need to do this myself and when I do – the need for friends will be gone and I suspect then my friends will be in touch.

My friends have been food and drink – they are a substitute for real happiness and loving relationship – Fatmea – my fat friend – you are relegated out of my league of friends.

THOUGHT FOR THE DAY
Being alone is not so bad, being alone with a friend is
better. Also – if you think about the negative things you
feel bad – if you think about the positive things, you feel
good. Don't forget the basics stupid!! Doh!
The sun is shining – last cut of the lawn coming up!!

FURTHER THOUGHT
Perhaps friendship is just about being yourself in good
company – enjoying companionship with the confidence
that if you needed help – you have friends that would be
there for you. If that's friendship – then I am blessed with
many friends.

14.11.2005   Day 53

Is this the real me?
Or an image of what I pretend
Who do you really see
What message do I send?

Is this the real me?
Can I find that place inside?
The one that says I'm free
Where even I can't hide

Is this the real me?
Do I really mean what I say?
It's not a lot to ask and plea
For truth and honesty I pray

Is this the real me?
Who knows, all I can do is try
To find myself and be
Who I am, that's me, no lie!

Why am I writing this diary? At first it was meant to be a personal journal of thoughts to give myself a little discipline on my journey to health without Fatmea. It is turning into something I think others may appreciate reading and in doing so, may give them hope, insight, courage to seek out their own path to happiness. Or is that just an ego trip of mine? Yes – OK. I would be pleased and feel good that someone else could read and value what I write here – but at the end of the day – I don't need to get it published. I would like one day for my family to read it, but at the moment I am nervous about world wide viewing. Why? This is my life, it's personal, it's me (as far as I can tell right now).

So, I don't know if this is the real me. We'll see!

THOUGHT FOR THE DAY (FINAL VERSE)
If this is the real me
Do you love what you see
And who really cares about who you really are?
Just be!

15.11.2005   Day 54

Tina (14 years old) was slashed with a blade taken from a pencil sharpener – her face needed 50 stitches, Caroline has just been released from hospital having had another girl (15 years old) attack her with scissors to her face, Holly has just been discharged from hospital having just recovered from trying to kill herself with an overdose.

These incidents have happened this week on the back of a report from our Children's Commissioner saying bullying is endemic in our society and almost every child is affected by it.

Bullying has always been around, but perhaps it is getting worse and particularly violent and amongst girls. If you were overweight at school, you probably fell into one of three categories: 1) you were bullied, 2) you were a bully or 3) you put your size to some good use and gained respect.

I was fortunate to be in Category 3 as I was a big teenager I played rugby and was quite useful – I was not a target of bullying directly, but often got challenged to fight the top hard man of the year above me – which I only did three times. Once I got a black eye and was knocked out, the next time I gave the other a black eye but felt guilt because he was smaller than me, the other – we made sure I won by getting together 5 of us to one. These were seen as rights of passage. It went on – you toughened up – you survived. It's less acceptable today, but more prevalent – why?

It doesn't surprise me – look at what we have, every second programme on TV has some association with violence, murder, police, crime, hospital drama etc. Most popular films are covered in bullets and blood. Combine this – now approaching second generation of binge drinkers brought up on x-rated video games, the softening drug laws or the re-classification of cannabis – which gave a mixed message – it's OK to smoke it just don't sell it! The eroding of teacher's authority – the fear of touching a child in case of getting sued, the lack of investment in parenting skills and the breakdown of the infrastructure related to spiritual and religious education – then it's no surprise we have a society where bullying is the norm.

It starts up in the home. If a child is brought up experiencing power, control and threat – and learning that this is the way to get what you want – then this will be passed on at school and eventually into the workplace. Those who use power, control and threat may use violence if the latter doesn't work. They use these things because that's their experience and/or they do not have the skills or awareness of using other forms of influence or communication.

They are now talking about asking children to fill in anonymous questionnaires in school to ensure the problem is identified – wrong!

Attention must be focussed in the home. My suggestion is that every bully should be taken home – and the family then be given support, training, counselling to understand how it happened in the first place and the dangers of passing this behaviour on to future generations, if not stopped now.

The bully at school should be helped to discuss his/her behaviour in groups with their peers and be given feedback as to how it's not clever and no respect is generated from it. What does a bully really need?

It usually boils down to attention, love and acceptance – then let's give it to them.

Fatties are bullied often – we are a soft target – it makes us unhappy, so we eat more! Children who are overweight are very vulnerable and as a society we must make sure they, and their parents, have all the support they need to reverse this disease.

This increasing trend in bullying horrifies and scares me – I feel sick to the stomach – why have these children chosen violence as opposed to tolerance, respect, love, learning, fun and happiness – what's going on?

THOUGHT FOR THE DAY
Are we becoming blind and disabled as a society because it's easier to be entertained by violence than to stop it!

16.11.2005   Day 55

Spent 4½ hours in a meeting yesterday! Trying to make a value-add contribution. I asked a lot of questions – but were they useful? Why do I ask questions?

- To clarify my understanding? No – I could have done that outside of the meeting if it was important.
- To challenge the others' perspectives – partly, this is expected of me, but not really effective.
- To offer observations and suggestions for improvement – again, partly, but not sure they were valued greatly.
- To demonstrate I understood, had a grasp of the situation, had done my homework and had some authority / status in the meeting – now that's more like it!

How difficult is it to keep the ego down? My fear is if I consciously kept my ego, or the external image of myself, in check – I would hardly say anything. Then people would question my value, my role, my contribution – but it's the nature of the ego to bow to others expectations as opposed to just being me. Is this the real me?

When I put that suit on and my ID badge – who do I become?

How many identities does each of us have?

I have:

- the business man / executive
- the consultant / trainer
- the husband
- the father, the step father
- the gardener
- the actor / singer
- the golfer
- the walker
- the couch potato, TV addict
- the writer
- the Disney fan
- the business class traveller
- the economy class traveller
- the brother
- the grandfather
- the nephew
- the uncle
- the drinker, party animal
- the student

- the lover
- the friend
- the grieving son
- the grieving brother
- the dieter
- the fat man
- the rugby union ex referee / fanatic
- the Lord of the Rings and Star Wars fan
- the 'not very good' DIY man
- the sentimentalist
- the author
- the dreamer, idealist
- the spiritualist
- the nurse
- the counsellor
- the helper
- the Mercedes driver
- the video / camera man
- the catholic, the Christian

Are these me or are they roles I play? What is the common thread? Has to be me. I am all these.

THOUGHT FOR THE DAY
What role would dominate today? How can being me be more?

17.11.2005   Day 56

Wrote to my old friend Graham yesterday. We were like brothers at one time, worked with each other, studied together, lived with each other, went on holiday together, often got drunk together, then I moved away. Then he got married again, so did I – and well – we hardly see each other. I do miss him. It was always fun and challenging together – it felt like us against the world sometimes and sometimes, it felt competitive between us. We used to teach together and he was always the one who would dominate and make the jokes and shock.

I would be the one who was generally liked (you either loved or hated Graham) and I invariably beat him at snooker and chess. I think this competitive element in close relationships, especially between men, is often very obvious and dominant but sometimes subtle, but always there. My sons, who are twins, are very competitive. Despite my best effort to reduce its importance between them, I realise I gave them a mixed message, because I encouraged them to be fierce in sport and to make it a big deal whether they can beat their old man at anything – snooker, cards, chess, bike riding, in the gym, arm wrestling – anything. It was always a goal. (Reminds me of my father bowling me out at cricket in a big parent versus pupils match in front of the whole school. That felt awful – I should have learned from that. Instead, we repeat and recreate patterns and events in our lives.)

So, I have encouraged competition – the importance of winning. It feels good to win – why? Because it somehow makes you better than the loser? There are times when I catch myself and can't take the game seriously, so have fun and cheat – declare it and lose, or lose deliberately and seriously so the other person feels better. Then I challenge myself and say no, that's disrespectful – you should treat your opponent with respect and try your hardest. Hardest for what? Beat him to smithereens! I suspect within the dynamics of competition are the seeds of conflict. It's a separation – us and them – and as in all differences, this can lead to one fighting the other. I realise now I am a lot less competitive and it's not the winning that's important, it's doing justice to the game, playing my best, that's why I enjoy golf so much – it's a challenge of my mind, body and spirit every time I attempt to hit that ball!

Back to my friend Graham – I think in our separation, I am aware of wanting to tell him how well we are doing and keen to know how they are doing. Is this competition? No, I don't think so. It's more of maintaining connection through our joint work and interests we used to have, and maintaining respect for each other. It's not a strong need, it's more of a throw-back to what we used to have. We were, after all, soul mates for a while. Perhaps I need to let this go as well. Old images of good things that are no more – move on and create something different. What do I want? What new relationship do I want to create?

This is a key question running throughout this diary. Letting go, moving on and creating a new relationship.

THOUGHT FOR THE DAY
What new relationship do I want with myself and the world?
(WID tomorrow – steady week – hope to have lost a couple of pounds!)

18.11.2005   Day 57

Oh dear – I thought this week I have been careful. So, what's gone wrong? I have for 5 mornings done my exercise – in fact on two occasions I increased it from 20 to 30 minutes. Breakfast has been cereal or fruit, lunch has been a salad or soup and evening meal has been meat and 2 or 3 veg, and a yogurt and apple. Extras include the occasional packet of Quavers (40 calories), extra apple, Ryvita biscuits, couple of glasses of wine on an evening. Maybe it's the extras, or the portions. Cereals can be very calorie heavy – OK – thing is not to get despondent – I am eating a lot healthier and have to remind myself at least I am not putting weight on. And, to be honest, this regime of eating what I want just less has been very easy – maybe this is the plateaux people talk about, where your body starts to get used to the weight loss you have already achieved, before losing more, which is better than losing it quickly.

So far I have lost 22lbs, only 1 more this week. This weekend I am taking my wife to Barcelona for her birthday, so the temptation will be high. Sensible eating can still win. Fatmea so far, I feel, has been kept in control most of the time.

Energy in must be less than energy out – so keep up the exercise and keep off the snacks and reduce those portions! Time to re-read some of my diary – keep motivated and remind myself what this is really all about.

I got this call on the ward I was working on as a young staff nurse many years ago! The call was from reception. It was Easter Sunday and the receptionist and I always had a good relationship. She said that I have better come and meet Jesus Christ, he wanted to ask someone about a bed for the night. I said she must be bored and to get back to her magazines. No, she said, seriously, this is Jesus Christ here – come now! I decided to play the game.

At reception, I met Jesus – real name David – but he was Jesus today, with sandals, and a white sheet wrapped around his shoulders. He stared through me and said "I am lost, I need shelter, I am the son of God'. Now how could I refuse – I took him in – he was admitted as a voluntary patient.

David became very violent, attacking several of our staff and patients – sadly he had to be sedated and secluded. He was in his early twenties and a trainee police officer. An incident I will never forget was going into his room – there always had to be two of us – he seemed calm, and on this occasion looked at me, not through me and called me by my name.

I said I had come to empty his piss-pot, he said fine and bent down to hand it to me. With that – he threw what was a full pot all over me, full frontal in the face. There was a moments' silence between us, we froze. I said thanks, walked out – he howled with laughter. That was the start of a beautiful relationship!

David suffered from temporal lobe epilepsy – and once on the right regime of drugs, be became stable, enough to eventually be discharged. I got a phone call some months after he was discharged – it was David, he wanted to meet for a drink. Not usually a good idea in those days to meet patients after discharge, but this was different. We met in a pub just outside York – he was great, all he wanted was to say thanks, relive the piss-pot moment and say sorry, and to let me know he was re-joining the Police Force. Now that's a success story!

THOUGHT FOR THE DAY
If Jesus Christ presented himself today, would we admit him to a mental health hospital?
You don't need a miracle to lose weight, just less food!

19.11.2005   Day 58

We were on holiday in Spain a few years ago and one evening, in a restaurant as usual, the street peddlers came to sell their carvings and counterfeit bags, watches, glasses etc. These are charming people and you only have to make eye contact with them and you will find yourself in an intense negotiation just debating whether you need anything at all.

I was feeling playful that night, and to the horror of my wife, I asked to look at the carvings – he then gave me a price of 20 Euros – and we had great fun beating this down with all sorts of wonderful stories about his poor family. Eventually, he agreed to 5 Euros, I gave him a €5 note, but said I didn't want the carving. I was just grateful for the fun. He looked shocked, we walked away.

On our way home that night, on the pavement not far from our hotel near the main road, something caught my eye – it was a €5 note – spooky? I put it in my wallet. A few days later, we visited a church in the mountains in a beautiful white village called Mijas – said a few prayers for our mothers and my sister – and I put the €5 in the charity box. A year later, when we were on a weekend break in Dublin, a street beggar and child approached me – I said I had no change, I was about to pay for a newspaper. I had a €5 note. I paid for the paper, thought nothing of it, then just as I was returning to the hotel the same woman caught my eye – I gave her the change from the €5. Ever since, without deliberately thinking about it, I have always had either £5, $5 or €5 note in my wallet and if something spontaneous happens regards a request for that money – I give it. I suspect I will always have it to give.

This week in the UK is a national fundraising week called 'Children in Need'. Every year, the country raises money for our children's charity in the UK by doing all sorts of sponsored activities from going to work in fancy dress to having your chest and back waxed free of hair (no thanks!). Around £35 million will be raised. We have another week of fundraising called 'Red Nose Day' or 'Comic Relief' where we all put plastic noses on, have a day of not taking life seriously and raise the same sort of amount for causes often related to children, but internationally as well as UK.

We give to these, plus every time there is an appeal for a disaster.

We also sponsor a child in Africa, and we support our friend who works in Africa, also any friend who wants sponsoring and we support our Cancer Charity BACUP. Every day we get at least 3 requests for more money, and every day I feel we haven't given enough!

My wife thinks I'm crazy, but I just feel we don't need as much as we have compared to what others need right now. She then reminds us that we may need it in the future when our income runs out – mmmm? Well – I think those with a charitable heart will never be short of wealth, and if we all gave a little more, the world would be a better place. I rang up the charity line last night to try and get a message to the presenter Terry Wogan – to ask – what's the chance of asking people to donate 10% of what they have given to children in the UK to children in Pakistan as their need is greater than ours. The kind person on the phone said they would pass it on – well, at least I tried.

I sometimes challenge myself in all this – does it make a difference giving money to charity – where does it actually go – am I feeding an administrative machine or are people really benefiting? Anyway – isn't giving money just a way of easing my own conscience? If I really cared, I would be out there helping wouldn't I? Guess there is a limit to my charitable heart!

This diary feels very self indulgent – I hope something good comes of it.

THOUGHT FOR THE DAY
Think less of yourself and more of others.

20.11.2005　　Day 59

Here we are staying in a hotel in one of the most famous streets in Spain – La Ramblas – this is the place to stroll, market stalls, shops, artists and street entertainers every step of the way. What a night to arrive! Two of the best soccer teams in Spain playing each other – Barcelona away to Real Madrid. The streets at 8pm were half empty, the bars full.

We knew the result when we heard the car horns going. A famous victory for Barcelona 3-0.

The noise was incredible. Our window overlooks the street so we could see crowds gathering, then hear bangs and singing. We decided to take a closer look.

The street was full, packed – we could hardly move. Police blocked part of it, they were jumping, chanting, red flares were lit, fireworks were ignited – it seems that everyone with a flag has come out in their car to show their flag and pap their horn!! The nationalistic pride and joy was exciting, but also a little frightening too!

We sat in the window that night watching the celebrations and the street entertainers – then in contrast to the chanting and car horns, we heard melodic pipes and drums. Just in front of us, a band started playing – they must have been North American as they wore Indian head-dress and were dancing a traditional American-Indian dance. It was surreal – two ends of the street, two very different cultures – yet both tribal and dancing!

> ### THOUGHT FOR THE DAY
> *If only people could see how similar we all are!*
> *PS: Had too much wine last night! It's easy to get caught up in the excitement of the occasion – must learn to celebrate without drinking.*

21.11.2005   Day 60

Lighting candles in the Cathedral for a moments grief for our mums, witnessing the flickers of light in the shadows of the Madonna. Climbing to the top and feel the sun on our face whilst breathing in the majestic views. Taking a cable car from romantic gardens to the golden beaches. Getting lost in the ancient corridor of the gothic old town and being surprised by the spiritual openings into yet more beautiful testimonials to the human spirit. Relaxing stroll through the Spanish village and being mesmerized by the modern artists amongst the 'Picasso' and 'Dali'. Finishing the day off in a stark contrast with hard rock and nachos! What a day!

But what actually was the highlight – the touch of the hand, the gentle kiss, the loving and tender heart of the one you love by your side, sharing and delighting in the experience. Who needs food and drink when this menu of life is on your doorstep?

THOUGHT FOR THE DAY
Take a trip across the water or borders and drink in the
rich cultures and let the experience feed your soul.

22.11.2005   Day 61

Please, please, please – whoever you are reading this – do me, yourself and the world a favour – visit and experience the majesty and splendour of the unfinished cathedral.

The only cathedral currently being built – and built in the images and vision of a man called Goudi of Barcelona, who clearly had a sense of what the human spirit represented and at the same time, had the knowledge and skill to build something that represented this human soul.

Whatever your religion or beliefs, what we have here is a testimony to what is the birth of life, the passion of death and the hope for everlasting life. All this connected with earthly representation of fruit and trees, sculptured to represent life as is and as it could be.

This cathedral can be our monument to peace – against all the odds. You must visit the Familia de Gradia.

Today is my wife's birthday – she doesn't want to get old. She feels young. She wants us to go on forever, and so we shall.

THOUGHT FOR THE DAY
If you could see and touch the human soul – what
experience would this be?

23.11.2005   Day 62

At the age of 14, Picasso was showing his paintings and impressing the great and good. Here is another example of a great talent, able to communicate the inner soul through creative media. The Picasso museum illustrated his great works through his life and one could see how his expressions changed and his interpretations of what he saw changed, yet this phenomena is best explained in his own words 'I do not develop, I am'.

The flight was diverted because of fog at our home airport – the fog cleared so we took off again – double risk, in the hands of God and the pilot – it was a heavy landing in almost nil visibility. It's always good to be home!

Fatmea has been kept in order pretty well whilst away. Walking and taking in the sights all day, and not being too lucky with choice of restaurants, meant energy has definitely been greater out than in!

Visiting the cathedrals and churches in Barcelona remind me of my most favourite Cathedral – St Paul's in London (apart from the York Minster of course – special because it is my home town and loved by my mother, oh – and St Peter's Basilica in Rome, because there Mave and I were blessed by Pope John Paul).

When I worked in London for a short while in the heady days of being a Telecom executive – I often sat in St Paul's Cathedral – for peace, quiet and reflection – I wrote this one afternoon amongst the chaos of life:

I rest a while in magnificent splendour
In touch with unearthly things
The vastness of my void
Shouts at the future and cries for the past
My love is immeasurable, my gift unending
Receive it and live

74000 dead in Pakistan, 100's of 1000's, dying of starvation in Niger, deaths everyday in Iraq, atrocities to each other every day around the world.

THOUGHT FOR THE DAY
'I am' seems so insignificant – yet I believe it is our only hope.

24.11.2005   Day 63

If you live in a certain part of the UK and are defined as clinically obese by your Doctor – ie you have a Body Mass Index of 30 or more

– then you will not, even if you desperately need it through pain and disability, be put on the waiting list for hip or knee surgery! This is a big news story here as it is placed in the context of massive debts in our national health service. Now for me at 224 lbs and 6ft 1inch height then I am 29.6 BMI – whew – just under – that means I qualify! Last month I would have been over! To calculate your Body Mass Index, take your weight (in kilograms), and divide by your height (in meters) squared.

Rationing in the health service has always gone on. It's just now, through freedom of information, the open public values and increased public expectation that the criteria for making these decisions of who gets treated for what with what becomes more discussable. When there is limited resource do you choose to treat patient A who has a 75% chance of benefiting from the operation or patient B who has a 25% chance? I believe this rationing process was one of the factors that played a part in my sisters' decision to stop kidney dialysis which led her to a slow coma and death.

I think the refusal of treating obese people seems a little harsh, however, if these people are offered counselling, group support, food education and exercise clinics to achieve a target weight in order to have the operation then this could be a more effective way of approaching the health of those who are 'obese' and in need of this type of surgery. If we extend this principle then I suppose those who smoke should be lower on the list to be treated for lung and heart disease and the obese should be lower for treatment of high blood pressure and diabetes.

The heavy drinker certainly shouldn't be given a liver transplant. This last point is very topical at the moment as one of our first celebrity footballers – George Best – is currently dying in hospital through liver failure. However, I think his transplant may have been given because of who he was, so here is a man who has never been able to live with his fame – where his ego has dominated – and he has lived an image and struggled to find himself – should he have been given a second chance to live? Now, of course none of these cases are black and white, and each case should be considered individually. It does raise the issue of course – how do we in the UK continue to afford a health service which continues to be free at point of need. I believe as a nation to continue to enjoy a free health service we have to take our health a lot more seriously. We must break the dependency most people have on our health service and the expectation that no matter what our status – we will get the best possible care available. This has never been entirely true anyway because the more educated you are, the more assertive you are and especially if you know someone in the health system – then you will find a way to get up the priority list for treatment.

Every day more expensive treatments are becoming available. Herceptin for breast cancer for example. £44,000 per treatment – can we afford it – tell that to the woman who has just been diagnosed!

THOUGHT FOR THE DAY
Within the next few days George Best will have died – he will be remembered as a great footballer and an alcoholic who beat his wife up and didn't respect his new lease of life with a new liver! How do you want to be remembered?

25.11.2005   Day 64

Yesterday our government relaxed the licensing laws – hooray! This means now an 18 year old can drink non stop for 24 hours in a pub or night club that has the licence to offer this.

The case for? To stop everyone leaving clubs at the same time so drunk that they start beating each other up! So we stagger the closing times do we? Well, I'm not sure this will have the desired effect, ie: reduce drinking and reduce drink related crime? We will probably have the same amount though staggered over a longer period which will mean increased costs of policing and controlling – the jury is out – let's see?

WID tomorrow – I have definitely eaten less because of a cold, and I haven't exercised as much, but I think I have lost a few pounds – hope so.

THOUGHT FOR THE DAY
Patience, persistence and a determination to succeed!

26.11.2005   Day 65

Lost another 2lbs – this is good – gradual loss in the right direction. I seem to be eating less generally now and am not as hungry – nor am I continually craving or thinking of food. I believe I am moving towards a more healthy and balanced view of nutrition.

Last night we pulled off a real surprise for my wife in celebration of her birthday. We organised in secret all her friends and family to be together for a surprise party. I had to come up with a whole range of creative excuses to throw her off the scent and to convince her that it was really important to put a blindfold on! I came up with a story that, on our way to a dinner dance at a hotel, I wanted her to see a light display I had organised for her – but the effect would be much better if she was blindfolded. When I gave the signal, she took off the blindfold and she was faced with over 50 people who she knows – her face was a treat – a treasure – a pure moment of joy and the tears came flooding. My wife is one of those rare people who gives so genuinely her affection and tries so hard to help others and this was an opportunity for others to give a little back. I will never forget her dancing in the middle of all of us – just soaking the love that was obviously there for her – then her daughter dancing with her – what a beautiful sight! I am so lucky!

THOUGHT FOR THE DAY
**George Best is dead. How can we as a society protect
and support young talent so they avoid the path of self
destruction.**

27.11.2005   Day 66

Last night we were in the West End – doing one of our favourite things – walking around Covent Garden, listening to the street players, enjoying a meal then seeing a show. We saw Scrooge – the Musical – staring an aging but much loved star, Tommy Steel. Charles Dickens' story of Christmas will always be loved and the message of giving in order to experience joy will always be true.

I am now on a 747 to Hong Kong to deliver a Leadership Development programme. On the same plane is the famous British (Scottish) golfer, Colin Montgomery – someone else, who, I suspect has had a personal battle with his bulge and other demons. 11 hours flight – plenty of time to read, reflect and relax. Managed to shake Colin's hand (by the way – he won the Hong Kong open Champion at the end of this week – maybe I brought him a little luck!) and congratulate him on his great golf – strange, when you meet a celebrity in the flesh – I didn't approach him as a stranger – he must get used to the attention.

So, what am I doing here in Hong Kong? A small but hopefully significant piece of work. Helping a group of young executives, leaders of the future, to develop the appropriate personal skills and behaviours to motivate and empower others. A key ingredient in all this, of course, is to help them realise that personal power is not dependant on position, status or knowledge but in your ability to help others realise their own power. First, before the event, I need to listen to what's going on in the company and what's going on with the people I will be working with. Any development is only effective when it is directly related to the question people have about themselves. As in this journey – going back to day one – how can I lose weight was a key question made more significant and meaningful because I acknowledge it's my problem and within my power to change.

In Hong Kong it's so easy to get carried away with the hustle, bustle and glamour of big business. There are many people here full of their own sense of importance yet at the heart of this Chinese special province is a simple faith of love, acceptance, balance with a meditative quality linked to Buddhism, Tai Chi and many ancient Chinese customs. HK is, of course, multi-ethnic but you can't escape the depth of wisdom and history that is so much part of this culture. I can't help feel that the powerful forces in this land, of capitalism, political communism control, spiritual yearnings for freedom of expression and a younger generation with increasing expectations of what's possible, will all somehow clash in a chaotic mess. I pray somehow that a national evolution for the benefit of all this continent and the world, occurs and the Chinese contribute significantly to world peace.

28.11.2005   Day 67

Went out with friends last night. Wonderful conversations. One of my friend's wife is Korean and we started to talk about cultural differences in how, for example, when Korean people marry, the woman does not take her husband's name yet, from that day, she will be referred to as the wife of … and be rarely called by her surname. We also talked about men's inability to cry and I was championing the fact that some men can cry freely – our Korean lady states – 'but can you cry till it hurts like a thousand slices in your heart'! She expressed clutching her chest – the point was well made! There are, of course, degrees of expression and I did recall a time for me when I cried as if my heart was sliced – this was in a workshop as a participant where we were practising a meditative technique that involved slow and deep breathing. We were encouraged to tap into feelings, breath out, let a sound happen and then just experience the feelings. I ended up crying in a ball in a corner, unable to stop – I had, of course, for the first time given myself permission to grieve over the loss of my mother. I had cried inconsolably before – the difference here was that there was no attempt to suppress it, it was OK, it was a free expression of the pain, anger and hurt related to being left behind, alone and without the opportunity to love and hold my mother. It's amazing what pent up, unresolved, unexpressed feelings are inside of us and I suspect contribute to us not moving on if not expressed.

We also chatted about how some people like to be touched and some recoil at the very thought of it. Again the gender difference was dominant in our disclosures. One of my friends admitted his reluctance to embrace other men and a wish or desire to hug his father. He wouldn't do this because he believes his father would be uncomfortable with this. I think I was a little brutal in my challenge when I suggested he was projecting his own fears and in doing so denying each other a strong expression of each other's love.

I told the true story of when we were running a management development programme for 60 engineers – we were in this large hall and one of our team made an observation about how 'stiff', macho and inexpressive this bunch of men were. So, he suggested we made an announcement. "In recognition of the importance of today, we are going to celebrate it by giving one minute's intensive attention to 'National Hugging Day!" You could feel the tension in the room, and the colour drain from the faces of these steel men of engineering. With that we stood up and shouted – right, you have one minute to hug as many people in the room as possible – it was amazing – the noise levels, the sights of these men running around hugging each other – and believe me – a minute to hug is a long time – but boy did it break the ice and people still talk about it today, 20 years after the event!

To embrace another human being is a wonderful thing, to genuinely relax and feel the experience of warmth, love and friendship is too rare an occasion. Being comfortable with our bodies, our emotions, our willingness to be close and intimate with others are all wrapped up together here. Women tend to hug each other more than men – this is an inequality I would like to put right. I started last night – embracing my friend in manly bear hug fashion of course – as we said goodnight. The best hug I guess is when it's mutually given and enjoyed – well, I guess we have to start somewhere?!

THOUGHT FOR THE DAY
To touch is to bring us closer – why – whose need is this satisfying. How close will I be to people today, can I touch their hearts without embracing our bodies?

29.11.05   Day 68

Several times yesterday whilst working with colleagues I caught myself thinking – this is all stuff – stuff that isn't making a difference unless people really meet each other. Then I realised I was not meeting the people/person trying to communicate with me – so I try again and try to listen with the additional orientation – why is this person communicating to me – what's the main message? Then, just as we seem to be getting somewhere – something else happens, another person, phone call or email distracts and we are back to square one. Engaging with people in a busy work environment is a real challenge yet one I will continue to rise to.

Dinner last night at the top of the hotel, at the airport, overlooking the lights of Tung Chung and the harbour. Two friends, topics included us as fathers, our parents, our anxieties about our children driving, companionship into old age with our wives, reminiscing about us meeting and discussing our development and wondering if it was justified during work time – how times have changed!

World news, four peace activists captured/kidnapped in Iraq, the Vatican gets tougher on its approach to homosexuality and the enquiry into the Beslan school massacre points to mistakes all round. Tony Blair, our PM, speaking and arguing for the continuation of a Nuclear Power Energy strategy. So peace, sexuality, freedom and energy – world news – personal concerns!

THOUGHT FOR THE DAY
No matter how big the issues or complex the conversation – somewhere within it, we stand, we are touched, we are connected. How can I maintain a real sense of presence?

30.11.2005 Day 69

Pretty sure I am not losing weight this week! Usually do when I am working in HK – just this time every lunch time and evening so far has been around an invitation to meet someone – and because the food is there I have eaten it. The upside – I have not been hungry and eaten only at these times and small portions – downside – no exercise and each evening a pint of lager and a few glasses of wine. I feel it's all moderation and no weight gain and I feel good – so I am not giving myself a bad time over it. Also, my ability to listen to others; pay real attention to them and what's going on is also better than usual. I do feel different and conscious of a shift in my thinking and orientation to work, people and life. I re-tested myself (did the same test just over a year ago) using a psychological personality profile yesterday – and compared with just over a year ago a shift has occurred – it shows me being more 'frank' – tendency to be more blunt. I relate to this as more challenging when listening – I am asking myself what the purpose of this conversation is – what is the meaning of our meeting and if appropriate checking it out – I guess this could be seen as 'frank' or blunt or to the point. It's just that I sense in me the need or wish to make the most of every moment and every relationship.

THOUGH FOR THE DAY
Making a difference means being me and really listening.

01.12.2005   Day 70

Disturbing call from home! Apparently someone has bought our home in Florida without us knowing about it. It seems we are victims of identity and property theft! At best we are going to have to spend thousands of dollars securing our deeds and proving fraud – at worst – our house could be sold on, re-mortgaged and we get to fight the lenders for our equity. The Florida home is our pension fund – to lose this means either me working till I drop or living very frugally. My wife is having to deal with this on her own – I go back home tomorrow night – it's a stress and worry we could do without and will probably be the trigger to sell up – if we manage to salvage the situation. Apparently this scam is on the increase – it's amazing what you can find on the internet, about who you are, your details, your transactions etc – we have seen the property deeds with our 'forged' signatures on that says we have sold it!

Oh dear, what a shadow on what was a great day from a work point of view and connecting with people.

We really don't know the damage or the trouble we are in yet – early stages – we are going to have to rely on our contacts in Florida to help us out. Watch this space!

THOUGHT FOR THE DAY
Don't let being a victim sour your faith in humanity.

02.12.2005　Day 71

Well, our worst fears realised. This person, Mr CV, has recorded a forged deed with fake names, addresses and probably fake notary and used the deed to re-mortgage the house for $147,500 – then what happens is he doesn't pay the mortgage and the lender forecloses. Some people don't realise this has happened until the house is taken off them! Luckily we have found out early because my wife is super organised and on the ball so decided to ask why we hadn't had our Real Estate Tax bill (Council Tax in the UK) – reason – because we don't own the house according to the records!!

We have also found out that this con artist (CV) has done the same thing to a neighbour of ours – only he has done it to the people they sold their house to and there are now two sets of deeds recorded for the same house!! All this can be seen and printed out on the internet! There is something fundamentally wrong with the system.

With the Floridian recording system of house ownership it means anyone can submit a crude forgery resulting in thousands of dollars lent by the lender and possibly the house taken away from the original owners through default of payment.

Why don't the recording office spend one minute checking the validity of the addresses – or the commission number of the notary – we did – it literally look a few minutes to discover they were obviously fake. Why don't the lending company do this to stop this level of fraud so the incentive to forge these documents is lowered? Why didn't we know about this? Apparently we were vulnerable because we "paid off our mortgage" – if we had a mortgage it would have been recorded and more difficult for the con artist to forge or make a case for a further mortgage.

Something good must come out of this – we must warn people and I wonder if Jeb Bush knows that a fundamental right of the American people is at risk here – home ownership in Florida is beginning to look like a joke – and once this news breaks – then property will slump. If we get our home back – we are selling up – we have had enough!

Now, when I feel a little irritated, upset or angry – I sometimes lose that awareness and consciousness of who I am, and what's really important. So tonight, after a hard day's work and this exocet missile hurled into our lives, I would usually over-indulge before getting the plane home at midnight. I must catch myself, take a deep breath, and recognise – this is life – deal with it – there are many people in this world who have no roof over their head and I'm getting upset because one of my roofs is under threat!

THOUGHT FOR THE DAY
Get real!

03.12.2005   Day 72

World Aids Day! Many still dying – mostly those in the third world and those living in poverty. Apparently 70% of HIV positive in America live in the Deep South and are of African/Caribbean descent. What's it going to take to change this – why haven't resources been poured into this area – education, counselling, support for work and housing – the richest nation in the world yet it's home to the poorest.

A prayer for the young Australian who has just been executed by the Singaporean government. He was caught with 400 grams of heroin. His life story, his relationship with his twin brother show him not to be a bad person, nor a drug trafficker – yet this mistake cost him his life. I cannot support the death sentence – too many innocent people have been killed this way and as a human race – we should not legalise killing each other in any form – as a deterrent it is not proved – so what is it for? God rest his soul.

Celebrated a good week's work with a meal at the airport with friends and work colleagues. Good to relax, good fun, too much drink – but probably less than normal. Shadow over me wants to get back home as soon as possible so I can be with and support my wife. We now have copies of many transactions made by the same person who has conned us out of our Florida house. We have his mortgage record, criminal record, driving licence – all taken from the internet. Our son Myles is a whiz at getting the technology to work wonders. All the information is now passed on to an Attorney we have hired – on trust – retainer fee of £1,000 sent! The cost and the battle now starts.

I know I haven't lost weight this week – I don't want to weigh myself – denial? No just no point. Back to it now in earnest. Also – I can start back on the exercise regime. Just read that now there is even stronger evidence that exercise reduces the likelihood of breast and bowel cancer and probably many other types of cancer.

THOUGH FOR THE DAY
Being home means being close to the one I love most.

04.12.2005 Day 73

Home is ...

- embracing your wife so hard so we could feel each other's heart beating and I feel her body relax into tears of relief
- having my 15 month old grandson arrive and immediately run into my arms with a smile and a sense of who I am
- sitting in my favourite chair watching my favourite sport on TV at the same time listening to my wife competing with the TV happily telling me about the gossip and ironing at the same time
- inspecting my garden, seeing how it is surviving the winter winds, recalling the joys of planting and seeing it grow, planning to go out and tidy it up.
- sitting in the kitchen, drinking a lager and munching nachos and dip whilst chatting to my wife as she cooks chicken curry.
- getting up to speed with everything in my wife's world so we can work together, support each other and be stronger.
- getting a text from my son to say "welcome back Dad"
- talking to my step daughter to start planning Christmas surprises.
- getting the Christmas decorations out and the tree prepared
- sitting, struggling with staying awake and caressing my wife's feet whilst watching X-Factor and I'm a Celebrity Get me out of here!
- the familiar bed and the familiar position, sleeping in each other's arms.

Being rich and wealthy means being able to give and receive love – being super rich and wealthy means doing this with someone you love in your own home.

05.12.2005   Day 74

I watched a programme on psychic ability last night and they gave out a test for the viewer. You had to predict which colour or symbol out of 5 would be repeated, then you had to guess what a person was thinking, smelling or tasting or feeling – again 5 examples – maximum score would be 10. I got 9 – in fact I think I would have got 10 if my wife hadn't shouted out the same answer I was going to choose. Does that make me psychic – I doubt it – but I do believe we are capable of a lot more than we think.

There were hardly any animals killed when the Tsunami hit – they sensed it coming and moved to higher ground. Dogs can detect electrical disturbance in human brains up to 40 minutes before it begins to become so bad it results in an epileptic fit; dogs can also detect cancer cells. So, if this ability is in animals, why not us? I think potentially it is. We have over years become dependent on material and technological comforts to make our life easier, we just don't use it. The American Indians, Australian Aborigines and many other ancient tribes today still hang on to human ways of sensing and healing that have long been lost in most of us.

I believe it is possible to develop these again through use, belief and concentration.

London Taxi drivers were scanned to see if their brains were different to most – indeed the part of the brain responsible for sense of direction and planning, called the hippocampus – was larger than most. This shows if you use it you can grow it! I do believe we have other abilities and perhaps a 6th sense. I sometimes think of someone then they phone or email. Other sensations include an awareness of another presence – some other energy other than my own – this can be related to actual people I can't see or just my own projection. When I am quiet or praying or exercising and close my eyes – I can see or sense my loved ones around me, those who are dead and often those I haven't seen for a while. Many people will say this is all creative imagination and perhaps it is – but what if it was the seeds of an ancient human ability to sense, predict, heal and connect with the spiritual world?

There are many cases of where people have been given months to live – but through the power of their own thought, belief and positive behaviour – heal themselves – and the tumour or cancer disappears. Medically they would call it "in remission" – but there are too many cases of this to say 'we got it wrong again – they should have died'. I believe the power to heal ourselves and others through positive thought and human touch is phenomenal. I remember when I was training to be a therapist – we had a healer from Mexico to describe his approaches – we were walking around the room, breathing loud and laughing – then quickly sitting and listening to each others experiences. I recall doing this – then all of a sudden my left eye went so blurred – I couldn't see – I panicked a little – he came over, placed his hand over my eye – the heat and gentle touch I remember – and after a few seconds he released his hand, he didn't even ask if I was OK, he just walked away and I could see – I was OK! Don't ask me what it was all about – but it happened. There are too many cases of people being healed by visiting holy sites, for example Lourdes. Whether this is down to the spirit of the Virgin Mary or God touching our souls and healing our bodies or more likely – something in us is released – a power of belief that communicates to every cell in our body – saying – heal, and it does!

The power of self belief and the ability to connect to others is phenomenal. Let's do it!

THOUGHT FOR THE DAY
If Jesus could do it – so can we! Let's try and work a little miracle on ourselves and others.

06.12.2005   Day 75

Flicking through some old papers and I found this:-

Pomp and ceremony
Pride and joy
Relief and disbelief, is it really time
Once born a humble school boy
Now a University graduate
Flowing cloak and smiling faces
Name out loud, I stride my paces
Bow and shake
Receive and wake
To the splendour of award
A certificate of merit
My heart leaps with joy and sadness
For those whose spirit is in my saying
Well done love
Well done son
Well done our kid
And bow to the drive life has given us
What next they ask
We'll see.

I wrote this in December 1990 after receiving a Masters Degree at Leeds University. This was after 3 years of part-time study and research whilst I was a Manager in a Telecommunications company. Boy was it hard work. Doing a full-time job at the same time squeezing in degree study is enough to put you off academia for life! It did me. This was the end of years of study – from the age of 18 to 35 there was hardly a month where I wasn't studying for something. Nursing, teaching, psychology, psychiatry, counselling, business etc etc! Why? What was the drive? I've always enjoyed learning and striving towards getting better at what I do so I can be in a position to make a difference. Going for the qualifications and achieving the recognition was an additional incentive and the structure of study helped in the discipline of learning. The qualifications and status, certificates on the wall are not important – however, the experience has helped me develop an eclectic feel and value for the mysteries of life. I think this drive is still strong in me and hence this diary – trying to make sense of my own personal journey towards health and fitness. But there is more to it than this. I feel I have re-created myself – from being at the peak of my success in business terms to recognising it not being important – I have ceased driving looking for work and concentrated more on just being me. This feels different. It feels like I am at the early stages of a new career! The work still comes in but my orientation to it is different – it's changed from how can I do a good job so it generates more – to – how can I touch these peoples' lives so it makes a difference for them.

THOUGHT FOR THE DAY
What's it going to take to get a certificate for living – I mean really alive – life – living!!

07.12.2005   Day 76

The joy and energy in looking after our grandson for two days in the middle of the house upside down with half finished Christmas decorations. At the same time, I am catching up with the demands of business having returned from a challenging afternoon's critical meeting, planning to leave for a 3 hour drive to run a workshop, still tired from jet-lag against a back drop of feeling victimised and bruised with having our identity and property stolen – there is no wonder my wife and I start shouting at each other because I couldn't get my head round who to and who not to send Christmas cards to this year!! I just wanted to get in the car right then and leave – but no – we caught it, recognised it – hugged and made up. So much for in the moment, awareness, being conscious, calm and peace to everyone! I was bloody angry! So where did that come from? My wife, who is from Italian descent from a beautiful mother (God rest her soul) has no problems in venting her feelings – I guess I haven't as much, so when I do a bit of a volcanic reaction occurs. It shows that there is still much anger in me which I know relates to past traumatic events and if I hadn't faced up to these and expressed my anger before, I would be concerned. I know and have mentioned in this diary previously that blocked, unexpressed negative emotions can stop you moving on, inhibits learning new ways and limits your belief in the happiness you deserve.

I do a self check from time to time – and I believe I am OK – I have no limiting beliefs and I can be happier everyday as long as I stay connected to who I am and recognise the potential for greatness in all of us.

So the run up to Christmas starts. Fatmea loves Christmas – I am going to have to give her a good talking to and remind her she is on her way out – not to get comfortable and to recognise what is really important at this time.

THOUGHT OF THE DAY
If Jesus can lose his temper then so can I – but let's be clear what the anger is really about. Focus it not at another but use it as a door to understand more about who you are.

08.12.2005   Day 77

Had to work quite hard yesterday. One of those 'one man show jobs' from 8.30am to 6pm. I said to a colleague of mine after work – I am really tired, I wonder if the jet lag is still having an effect – he replied – no, it's your age mate – you're no spring chicken – 51 is getting on a bit!! We forget – and still think we're 30 inside – yes – I do too! But I can't accept that at 51 I should be so tired after a full day's work. OK, I haven't been sleeping too well and there's some background noise regards our Florida home – but getting old means getting tired easier?

I'm not ready to accept that – I know people a lot older than me and they still have the energy to perform, work, run etc. However, it's good to recognise how our energy levels change and to check out why. It's also good to recognise that tiredness equals vulnerability when it's so easy to over-eat and over-drink – eating was under control last night but one pint of lager and 4 glasses of wine was enough to send me to bed feeling a little tipsy and waking a little fuzzy! I must be stronger in these circumstances – I even gave myself a talking to before having any drink- which I suppose helped a little cos I did leave most of my last glass of wine. Oh dear – doesn't bode well for Christmas!

THOUGHT FOR THE DAY
Drink less, think young, be merry on the spirit of humanity, not on the spirit of alcohol!

09.12.2005   Day 78

Imagine all the people
Together as one family
Imagine all the world
Together one home
Imagine all the love
Limitless and shared
Imagine all the pain
Fleeting and forgotten
Imagine all the grief
Open and celebrating
Imagine all the wars
History and non-existent
Imagine all the wealth
Shared with hope and co-operation
Imagine life itself
Beautiful, engaging, peaceful and complete

These are not his words, but his inspiration. John Lennon was murdered 25 years ago yesterday. We need more peacemakers in this world.

THOUGHT FOR THE DAY
Some people may think I'm a dreamer, but I'm not the only one. Come and join us, so the world can be one.
Weigh-In Day – 220lbs – back on track!
(Total loss to date 25lbs)

10.12.2005   Day 79

The deadline from the kidnappers of the hostages – who happen to be peace activists against the Iraq war – has passed. Previous hostages have been beheaded on camera. Let us pray they are released and safe. God help them. The international climate summit is still trying to come to agreement on green-house gas limits. God give them the grace to make the right decisions for all our futures.

Woke up this morning with a very busy mind. Thinking about my health service responsibilities as a non-executive Director. Doing the right thing seems difficult, asking the right questions and being as open as possible is not welcome, giving feedback in a climate of learning is rare. So many people under stress, pressure and working in what essentially is a bankrupt system creates negativity and suspicion. My fear is that this could filter down to other staff and eventually compromise care. How can I support this current regime? I am not sure I can, and perhaps this isn't my time.

The Florida systems of home ownership and registration is flawed. I am drafting a letter to Jeb Bush and the Attorney General for Florida – surely there is a way to protect people from this.

Mave and I, over a couple of glasses of wine last night shared our hopes and fears for our children. The final analysis – be there for them, listen, share our words of experience and guidance as and when we can – pray that they are happy in what ever direction they choose and continue to express our love and support. And it's their life – let them go – it's our time – we must enjoy!

My dream last night involved me driving in snow and mud, I was skidding and sliding all over the place, I couldn't see where I was going, not moving very far and felt dangerous. Perhaps this is a metaphor for my non-executive role in the health service at the moment. In these circumstances, what do you do? Stop, wait till the weather improves. Then continue your journey in better weather – now there's the answer.

Today we finish preparing the house for Christmas and tonight we enjoy the company of good friends in our home.

Remember, psychological time, ie the time you spend thinking about what has passed, and the time you spend thinking about what might be – is time spent on things that don't exist. It also reduces the time available now. It's this moment that's real now, make the most of it!

11.12.2005   Day 80

Well done United States of America – at least you have joined the rest of the world in the fight against global warming even if you haven't agreed to targets – it's a start.

No news of our kidnapped peace activist Norman Kember – worrying.

My wife Mave has uncovered a mortgage scam that's been going on for over 2 years by the same person or gang. We now have to get this information to the appropriate authorities to stop them and protect others in the future. It's difficult so far away – I think a visit to Florida sooner than we planned is on the cards.

The sun is shining – the day has begun – what will it bring? I believe each day contains a surprise which adds to our joy and happiness – we just need to be alert and aware, sensitive enough to see it, connect to it, and experience it.

THOUGHT FOR THE DAY
How can I listen to the wisdom of my body and act out of love?

12.12.2005   Day 81

Massive explosion at an oil depot just north of London (Bunsfield). Hundreds of casualties, homes and cars destroyed. The main motorway is closed, planes diverted from the area. The smoke can be seen from space, the explosion was heard a hundred miles away and shook windows of houses 40 miles away. It's a miracle no one has been killed. I hope to God this is not a terrorist attack.

Oil is such a powerful and precious commodity. Wars are fought over it, lives are lost drilling for it, and it will get more precious and the conflicts are likely to increase as the world's oil reserves run dry.

My father worked in the oil business; he was a materials man on the oil rigs. The risks involved in this were highlighted by the Piper Alpha disaster in July 1988, with the loss of 167 lives. I had the opportunity to follow up on some of my father's connections, which resulted in me running an event on an oil rig in the North Sea. I wrote the following at that time.

What draws me to this fiery metal monster?
Standing unnaturally defiant against the wind and sea
No fear, no surprise, is this me or my father
Who steps from the bird to the pod strong and free
Dad, I want you to tell me again, the stories of oil,
The copter trips and mishaps that excited and scared you
Now I can touch, see, hear and feel aboard the Benloyal
Your experience is mine, bringing us closer
As a child I heard but did not listen
I created colourful pictures of your adventures
As a man I now know, the hardship and danger
The risks and comradeship that were there as an important part of your life.
You told me of adventure and danger
That kept you away from home and your wife
I could only guess and admire the flavour of life, then, yet now I know, how alone at times you were offshore amidst the men, metal and prone
to accident, pressure and much more.
Somehow I have created this option
I don't know why
But so many coincidences cannot lie
The purpose and meaning of me being there
Will no doubt become apparent
When it's time to design and share.

(My visit to the Ocean Benloyal - North Sea near the Piper/Claymore fields, 13, 14, 15 June 1990).

It's going to take days to put out the fire. It's the biggest fire in Europe since the second world war – no news yet of the cause. Thousands evacuated, risk of toxic fumes – what a disaster – just before Christmas too. It does seem that we can't go long before something to challenge our well-being happens, whether it's a personal problem or a world problem – life is about the joy and pain. It's important not to lose the sense of who we are during all the extremes of life, to live through the pain, learn from it and be stronger.

THOUGHT FOR THE DAY
Christmas presence! Can I gift wrap it and send?

13.12.05   Day 82

Now we have to pray for a type of wind to blow this cloud of polluted smoke away and disperse into the atmosphere. People already wearing masks. Warnings have been given to those with lung disease, asthma and heart conditions to make sure they have up to date medication and no-one really knows what the long-term effect of breathing in these poisonous fumes will have but the toxins are known to cause cancer!

I find it easy to get lost in the traumatic world events that seem to occur almost on a daily basis. Then we have things closer to home like the National Health Service – so big, so complex and is beyond managing on a large scale yet we are supposed to make local decisions in a national context. Then we have major fraud which affects us personally, ie loss of our home in Florida, and then we can either look at all this as a massive black cloud hanging over us as it burns now North of London, or we can thank our lucky stars and celebrate the fact that we are healthy, have loved ones who are also close and healthy and are going to have a happy Christmas together.

It's important to keep reminding myself that on one hand, yes, be concerned, send out positive thoughts and prayers to those in need, but continue to recognise what's important – who I am, my relationship with my loved ones and my health. Continue to be present in the moment, recognise the power of communication in terms of the truth and be confident in what you believe. I can only change and influence those things I have some control over – and that's only one thing – me and my reaction to, and relationship with, the world. This in turn will help me give full attention to those I engage with and if a moment of insight occurs that helps others – then I will be alert to it.

It's easy for your mood to be affected by depressing world events – it's easy to get into a type of thinking that says – what's the point, it's all depressing and it's going to get worse – this then can flip you into saying that about yourself and the next thing is your consuming large amounts of food and drink! Don't.

You can train your thoughts to be more positive – worse case – if you are feeling down – go for a walk, lift your head and look up – breath deeply – keep walking, then recall the good times and then focus on something you can see that's really beautiful. We do not have to be the victim of our thoughts and moods. We are in charge, I decide how I want to be!

THOUGHT FOR THE DAY
The more we are, the brighter we become, to lighten up what sometimes is a gloomy place.

14.12.2005   Day 83

The fire is still burning but under control. The American gangster/ murderer turned advocate for non-violence is to be executed in California. Race riots in Australia. And I don't think I have done well this week. Fatmea has just been kept under control but I have lost a few times. It's good to recognise the times when she will get an upper hand – after work – relax – evening – TV – socialising with friends. Are these also the times when I lose a sense of who I am and what's important – not sure – feels OK – feels like I'm enjoying myself – but at what cost. Managing to do about 5 times a week on the cross trainer for 30 minutes. I listen to either Paul Simon or Bat out of Hell or Enya whilst I'm exercising – depending on my mood. It's easy to go into a trance and think about connections, power, love, life, grief and feel good in the moment. It is important to get the old body working.

News item yesterday – confirmed, a third of Scottish children are obese. Majority don't like fruit and vegetables. This is the country that fries haggis and Mars Bars and eats them with chips! Now that maybe more calorific than the average McDonald!

The run down towards Christmas starts – today is my 'last delivery' – an action learning group for Managers trying to make sense of their world. Next week – a few meetings but then its concentrate on Christmas – great – I love Christmas. (So does Fatmea!)

Eat when you're hungry
Not when you're tired
Nor when you're moody
Especially if it's fried
Eat fruit and veg
Leave fat well alone
Don't hang over the ledge
Be fit and free to roam
You're better off being slim
Let love in and be
Not hours in the Gym
But recognise who you are – it's me!

THOUGHT FOR THE DAY
Why are you reading this diary? No – really – why?

15.12.2005   Day 84

Working in the National Health Service at a Senior Management level reminds me of playing chess with a paranoid schizophrenic.

Mark was in his early 30s and had been in a mental institution most of his adult life. He was the epitome of a mental patient image – a lunatic in an asylum; stereotypical picture (forgive me for using those labels).

His over large head was shaven, was 6ft with size 12 feet and over-long arms. He walked slowly, with deliberate over-long strides, often stopping and staring for no reason. His arms never moved when he walked and he had a hunch and stiff neck - probably due to the years of drugs to suppress what was a very violent history. When he looked at you - his steel, glazed glare went through you and he talked very slowly but deliberately and over-loud, only in response to questions and often in monotone and single words or short sentences.

Mark loved to play chess, but rarely found an opponent to play with.

As a young student nurse my colleagues encouraged me to ask him for a game - I did - and I was surprised to detect a slight grin in his response.

We started to play - he was quite good. I tried to make polite conversation - he grunted and continued to stare at the chess board. It was going well I thought, I'd got the upper hand, I took his queen and it looked as if I was on a winner. He stared at me, then the board, then at me - he then shouted at me "you touched my leg, you homosexual" then stood up and in doing so, sent the board and pieces flying. I thought he was going to hit me - my training said keep sitting, don't rise. I said I was sorry, I didn't mean it - with a quiver in my voice - Mark shouted some obscenity and marched off!! I'll never forget that game. Links to the NHS?

It's played with the best intention where the basic rules and standards are understood by all.

It can be played at various levels, but normally at its most complex.

The end game is rarely predictable until most of the pieces are moved.

You never know what the others' move is going to be - all though you spend a lot of time second guessing.

Mistakes are punished severely.

You move tentatively, hoping to get respect for playing well, but not to upset the powers that be.

And just when you think you have it sorted - you get accused of unreasonable behaviour and the board and pieces are thrown in the air, and you're faced with setting things up as they were before!

Mark was a particular favourite of mine, most staff and patients were scared of him. We did play again - it was OK. I knew the rules:

sit well apart and let him win!! I was devastated one morning to hear he had been found hanging from a tree outside our hospital church. It was a surprise – no one saw that coming.

Willie also suffered from schizophrenia but was old, frail and apparently harmless. He was 5' 2" and very skinny. He did have a colourful history where on regular occasions, normally related to a full moon (I kid you not) he would take his clothes off and go dancing!

If thwarted from this he would start throwing things – anything. I have never seen this before – it was now a rare occasion.

One morning as we were setting up for breakfast in the ward, Willie came in – looking far from old and frail – but with a spring in his step and a glint in his eye, and absolutely naked. We were told to encourage him to get dressed – mmmm! Well, that was difficult to say the least – with best intentions, I got a blanket, put it round his shoulders in a friendly way and said "Come on Willie, let's get you dressed" – with that he screamed a blood curdling noise, ran into the dining room and started throwing the cutlery at every thing and everyone. I've never seen him move so quick. We sent for reinforcements, the heavy gang in white coats came!

By this time, Willie was back in the dormitory jumping from bed to bed, performing some form of dance ritual. For his own, and others, safety, we had to grab him, restrain him and isolate him with sedation.

We jumped him – boy, was he strong! 3 to 1 didn't seem fair – but anything less – it would have been dangerous. We got him into the side room – now remember, I knew Willie as an old, frail, harmless, nice man – and here we were – 3 guys, average weight 16 stone – holding him down. I had his arms and shoulders, then I heard a voice "Oh, Mike, Mike – you're hurting me". I had never heard Willie speak and was so shocked he even knew my name – I felt awful and guilty – let go of my grip, then bang! Willie's fist was sunk into my eye and left his mark for some days after.

One lesson I will never forget – never underestimate the apparently disadvantaged or differently abled – they know and are aware of more than you think!

Not sure what this has got to do with me losing weight, but I do seem to be recalling events that made impressions on me. Maybe this is about acknowledging who I am and making sense of why I am the way I am.

What this diary is doing – is helping me in the fight with Fatmea – it has to be a daily reminder of what's important.

THOUGHT FOR THE DAY
We are not our past but we can learn from it for wisdom today.

16.12.2005   Day 85

Sitting in a warm ancient church at a candle lit round table. You could smell Christmas with mulled wine and the warmth of anticipation knowing you are about to be entertained by friends. Mave and I are members of our Musical Theatre society and last night we saw our friends tell the story of Dickens through his writings and the music from Oliver, Pippin and Scrooge. I love musical theatre – it combines the best of live acting and music into a drama that touches the heart. I have even dabbled myself playing Big Julie in Guys and Dolls, Bruce Ismay, the ship owner, in Titanic, and Chief Sitting Bull in Annie Get your Gun. It's amazing how professional these shows are, given that everyone works full time and the only rehearsal is each evening about 6 weeks prior to the show!

One technical, one dress rehearsal – then on – into the big theatre and run for 14 shows! It's tiring, challenging, great team experience but exhilarating. I felt the urge to write this after Guys and Dolls some years ago now:-

The pain, sadness, tiredness and rage
I carry daily this burden of mine
Yet to gather in song and dance on stage
Transports this grey gentleman to another time

The fun, laughter and tears of life
Can be condensed in a moment of fantasy
Yet to express ones true meaning and strife
Would open up scripts far too messy

For to come together with this band of strangers
And be a family of players
Is not without its risk and danger
For not all are talented balleters

Yet the dance of an elephant in its own way
Can capture the essence of drama by saying
The butterflies can flip yet the trunk can sway
The sparrows are singing
And the bulls do bay
But it's the cacophony of difference
that makes it rich and the chance
to be someone else helps me crawl out of life's ugly ditch

Yet we know when those notes go right
the steps do flow and the feelings expressed
that the stage has a life of its own

So I offer to you my fellow players
This verse to help us on our journey
So we continue to pass on our favours
to the audiences that continue to crave us.

I think its important to step out of your normal pattern of work, home, TV, out occasionally of your routine. Doing something new, with others, learning together helps remind us of the rich tapestry of life.

Everyone has their own story and some are more dramatic, traumatic and complex than others, but together – learning something new – we are all in the same boat – time to create something different.

It's too easy to get wrapped up in your own world – we all need a healthy balance and sometimes, that's achieved by giving good attention to others.

THOUGHT FOR THE DAY
What does it take to give real focussed attention to another?

Life is no rehearsal, every day is opening night!
WID tomorrow – hopefully no weight on, I'll be surprised if
I have lost anything!

17.12.2005   Day 86

Thought so – no weight lost this week. But hey, it's this time of year I usually pile it on. Christmas Extras! If I get through the next 2 weeks without putting weight on – that would be a minor miracle – let's try!

Last night – news item, it's official – 25% of UK men are obese. The pictures accompanying the news item were enough to spur anyone to lose weight. The giant naked fat bellies almost hanging over touching thighs. The large Double D cup men's breasts, the jellified legs – now thank the lord I am not as bad as that! A few months ago, 25lbs ago – I was in the danger zone – but now, on the road to healthy and slim. (Well, I don't think anyone will accuse me of being slim, but slimmer!)

I believe our personal power comes from within ourselves and not through control or seeking approval externally.

Approval seeking, being liked, wanting to be seen to be doing the right thing, getting/seeking positive feedback – these are probably my ways of seeking approval – they are not strong and I do catch myself, so I think I am winning on that one.

Control – doing what I want to do and creating the circumstances where that happens, being in charge, driving, reading the map, being on time, making suggestions indirectly to get what I want – I think that's it – again – it's a lot less than it was. I am much more relaxed and happier to go with the flow and I do catch and stop my self controlling. The alternative is to be in the moment, stop jumping ahead and making things happen, enjoy the present.

My business, I believe, has been successful because I planned ahead and made things happen – this is different – this is sound business – the trick is to do that without losing a sense of who you are in the moment. I know over the years there were many times I lost who I was – gave myself to work.

The consequences? Poor health and breakdown of marriage.

I worked with some managers recently – their stories are quite shocking. Average working week 70 hours + and available to be called in at short notice at weekends.

'What's stress' – 'I never get angry' – 'I will probably die young' (laughing) – 'I don't know what I want – what else is there?' – 'If I didn't do it, who would?'

These guys were trapped in the spiralling black hole of the work ethic – they were trapped. I replied:-

- "Organisations will always demand more than you can give. What ever you do will never be enough."
- "Who is choosing to work themselves to an early grave?"
- "IS this how you want to be for the rest of your life? What else is there other than work?"

I think the message got through to a couple of them.

So, personal power from within. Also, watch your stress levels and emotions – I lost out last night getting so annoyed with the poor communication and lack of proactivity from our Florida Attorney – I sent an email – very curt and business like – but resorted to some crisps and a couple of drinks! Ah well – it's Friday, end of the week – unwind, the old messages and habits are still there, they are tough to break!

THOUGHT FOR THE DAY
Less control, less approval seeking – more personal power from within!

18.12.2005   Day 87

Letter to Jeb Bush, Governor of Florida

Dear Mr Bush

Is the State of Florida colluding with fraud?

British owners of Florida property are victims of identity and property theft.

The following is a disturbing account and testimony of the legal systems and processes of The State of Florida.

On the 30th November 2005, we phoned the tax office to ask why we hadn't been sent a request for our Real Estate tax on our property. They informed us that the reason was because we no longer owned the property.

This is the property we bought in Kissimmee in 2003 with money we had saved for our pension because we love Florida and we hoped it would be safe and appreciate in value.

When we checked on Osceola County Court on-line records search, recording records shows a Quit Claim Deed as the owner to be someone else. Our signatures are forged, the witnesses are unknown, and the Notary seal and signature is also related to the con-artist who has apparently bought our home!

We also found out that there now exists a $147,500 mortgage on our property, taken out by the same fraudsters, who, by the way has many charges, court cases outstanding on his criminal record.

We find through further investigation that there are at least another 3 owners on our subdivision who have lost their property this way, and they all seem to be linked in some way.

This seems to be going on elsewhere in Florida and is getting worse.

Our questions are offered as a plea for help, sir, as I believe there is a lack of joined up thinking and security of information on your Government systems, legal systems and the MER system.

We now have to submit papers to fight for our property back. Some people don't find out they have a problem until they become aware of a threat of foreclosure on their home, due to a fraudulently gained mortgage on their house - which they technically no longer own.

1. *Why is it so easy to change ownership of a property by recording what are obviously forged documents? (It took us a few minutes to check the addresses of those on the documents and they don't exist)*

2. *Why is it so easy to get a mortgage or loan using these documents - why don't they do some checks as to the validity of the deeds?*

3. *Why haven't we be warned of this scam - why don't realtors offer advice as to how you can safeguard yourself against this happening? (If you can?)*

4. *Are there grounds for suing the County Court Office for negligence and for causing great anxiety and stress, as well as financial hardship incurred by many British Owners.*

We are now faced with significant legal costs to try and obtain legal ownership of our own home. We believe that this may undermine significantly the confidence in anyone buying in Florida and hence may affect the value of the property market and possibly the State economy.

As you read this, a fraud as recent as this week has happened after we have filed papers on the same people. It seems the fraudsters are a lot smarter and quicker than the legal system set up to protect us.

Please Mr Bush is there anyway you can set the wheels in motion to change the system so as it becomes safer to own a home in Florida.

Yours sincerely

Mr and Mrs Wash.

We now know this is a major fraud involving dozens of people working together. We now have informed the Attorney General, local Sheriff, and the FBI.

This was earlier this week - as yet - no response.

19.12.2005   Day 88

Cliff is a giant of a man and one of my best friends. At 6' 5", he stands out in the crowd, his deep but gentle voice conveys warmth rarely experienced. I met him in 1985, we were both working for a telecommunications company as trainers – his background was engineering, mine psychology – yet I sensed in him a depth of wisdom no psychology training could give.

We used to meet 4 times a year – seasonal – with 4 other fellow travellers. Just guys trying to support each other in simple questions like – are we making sense, how can we improve, what's the best way forward? Cliff was a great support to me in those days and we have met from time to time since we stopped our regular meetings back in the mid 1990's.

Cliff also had great way of bringing complex things down to its simplest level – at one meeting, he taught us to juggle!

Great times, fond memories. His partner rang up yesterday to say Cliff had only a few weeks to live, he was dying of stomach cancer.

I sent him my thoughts, recalling a very special two hour conversation we both had in a car, at a motorway service station. We met to discuss the meaning of God.

Remember our God conversation in the car?
We explored the unknown and our spirits soared
It was almost as if we could touch a star
And we knew who he was then, our Lord.

You are infinitely valuable so am I
You shouted out at York
You are someone I know couldn't tell a lie
And a friend who would rather walk and talk
Than wrestle with demons who have no chance
When friends get together and dance
with balls that juggle

and friends who struggle
To work out who they are and
What there is to do

It took some time for us to realise
That the answers were not too far away
Amidst the tears and joy he cries
It's you and me, now, today
This is the moment I will cherish
Knowing you will always be a gift of love
Our friendship without blemish
Your spirit will always fly as a dove
In the dawn of the day
In our heart you will stay

Love from your friend, Mike

He lies in a hospice now as I write – 300 miles away. I want to see him one last time.

THOUGHT FOR THE DAY
How vulnerable we are, how cruel this life can be – hang on to this precious moment.

20.12.2006   Day 89

Here I am, Hastings – on the South Coast – the last time I was here was nearly 2 years ago when my dear friend and his partner showed us around, talked of his childhood and the history of a place he loves.

I am rehearsing for grief, my heart is heavy, my tears flow freely, my efforts to recall all our times together is in overdrive.

I am no stranger to hospices. Last year, I was a regular visitor to my ex-secretary and friend, Fiona. She died of skin cancer at the age of 46 leaving a husband and two teenage children. Graham and I took her to the seaside in a wheelchair 2 weeks before she died. We walked along the front, the sea mist came rolling in – surreal. But that was the last thing we did for Fiona – what can I offer Cliff but my presence and everlasting friendship through prayer and thoughts?

It's difficult to prepare for moments like this – I just need to be there for Cliff and for me. It's a little frightening because in some ways, this is about me facing my own mortality. Cliff is about 10 years older than I, but his illness feeds one of my fears – he had to lose weight because of his diabetes, this masked other symptoms. He kept losing weight, until it was too late and secondaries had taken hold. Is this about Cliff or me? Now – shift – my love and attention is now for him.

My dear Cliff, my dear friend, you look so frail. You smile, clasp my hands, we both cry. He is pleased to see me and our warmth and affection for each other comes flooding back. Fed by tube, he speaks in whispers, drifting in and out, now on morphine.

We reminisce on some good times and I manage to read to him my poem for him. Cliff was an artist, a sculptor and loved working with his hands and appreciated creative expression.

We often used metaphors and symbols to describe feelings and moods. I asked him to describe what symbols or metaphors he would like to be remembered by. He described a field of wild flowers or poppies, swaying in a light breeze on a bright warm sunny day with the sky filled with white fluffy clouds.

For an hour, I held his hand. He slept a while, drifting dreaming, I could detect a smile, I could still see the giant of a man, his heart as generous as they come.

He knew it was time to go – he made it happen – let's do it he said – goodbye is hard to say. We hugged for the last time; we were both distressed – but better to face the pain than deny it. This is a lesson we both have learned.

Goodbye Cliff, you will always be in my heart.

I spent a precious, loving hour afterwards with Cliff's partner. We comforted each other, she gave Cliff a wonderful 5 years of companionship, the depth of love neither of them thought they would experience again.

Through tears she says "Cherish what you have, tell Mave you love her every day, it's so important".

21.12.2006   Day 90

The number of people classed obese has more than tripled in the last 20 years. It has been estimated that obesity accounts for 18 million days of sickness absence from work, and 30,000 premature deaths (where do they get their statistics from?). Each man and woman who's death could be put down to obesity loses on average 9 years of life. Treating obesity costs at least £500 million a year, and that the national costs of lower productivity is estimated at £2 billion a year. That's just the UK – multiply that up one hundred fold for the USA and that should grab the politicians attention!

So, what's the latest treatment? Swallow a balloon! Yes – swallow a balloon – fill it with saline. It tells you that you're full and doesn't allow so much food in. What a load of tosh!

They say trials done worked but it must be combined with a 1000 calorie a day diet, and after the balloon has been removed, then weight loss is only maintained if the behaviour / life change is adopted. And we pay people to tell us this??

(Cliff is on my mind and in my thoughts continuously – I know this shadow will be with me for some time – I must turn it into a strength and celebration of his friendship and life).

Well, back to it – blew it last night of course – after such an emotional day, went out for a few drinks and an Indian curry with my wife, our secretary and my step daughter. It was a pleasant diversion. They are great company.

The diversion doesn't last long! I don't want to die slowly like Cliff – several months in hospital then weeks in a hospice – and I would rather die at home I think – who knows, god this is morbid – get off it. Remember Christmas is around the corner. This is a celebration of new life, a renewal of all that is good in humanity.

THOUGHT FOR THE DAY
No thoughts, just feelings.

127

22.12.2005   Day 91

Christmas – I think I'll rename it emotion-mas – it's almost like we store up our feelings all year long, then over a few days, the tap is turned on, listening to carols, watching old films, thinking of loved ones passed, catching up with friends and family not seen all year round and I feel dull and drained and seek solace in food and drink!! This has been my life long pattern, and now my children expect it of me and soon it will be my grandchildren.

One year, I might just break the pattern and do something completely different – but not this year.

But something needs to be different this year to avoid piling on the weight – so what's it to be? A few things I have found useful and mentioned before here in this 'journal of life':-

- Breathe deeply, stand outside of yourself, look at yourself and ask what's important right now?
- Keep asking why am I eating or drinking right now?
- Remind myself of my personal vision.
- Focus on the now – this moment – be conscious
- Receive the love around you by really listening, paying attention and follow through on intuition and coincidences
- Keep up the exercise 30 minutes each morning

Close the office early today – final buying of presents and then the countdown to a wonderful time of year – let's not allow the shadows of grief and conflict darken the light and joy – in the end, the brightness will win through.

THOUGHT FOR THE DAY
In the blink of an eye
Life passes by
Don't waste your time
In the past with rhyme
Nor the future that may be
As it is now that matters
You and Me.

23.12.2005   Day 92 (Christmas eve eve!)

Of Christmas past, stockings, socks and pillow cases full of sweets, toys and fruit, mysteriously on the end of the bed as we wake with excitement and disbelief. Childhood memories of Christmas are full of vague delights but all with a sense of excitement, happiness and wonder. Snowball fights, sledging, ice slides, Christmas lights, chocolate money, searching for presents before Christmas hidden by mum somewhere, midnight mass, candles and incense, visiting the crib, opening one present after mass, the turkey – going on forever, the lunch, what a feast, the TV, a wonderful life, I'm dreaming of a white Christmas, never stop eating! Boxing Day – the whole family – Christmas Day again – aunties, uncles, cousins, more presents, great fun.

I am so blessed to have had such wonderful and plentiful childhood Christmases. More recently the delight on my boys' faces on Christmas morning between the ages of 3 and 11 – after that the magic tends to wane a little for them.

Singing carols around town on Christmas eve, getting better as the evening goes on as we move from hotel to pub, to pub! Sitting with my wife Mave and my step children opening presents to Christmas Number One songs.

This year, some change – for the first time, our son (my stepson) is staying with his girlfriend on Christmas Day and we will have a visitor for a couple of hours – our Grandson!

I'm struggling this year to buy my boys anything meaningful for Christmas – but it's just come to me – sitting here reflecting – it's to do with their journey, their travelling – St Christopher on their key rings – yep! That might, over time be appreciated. (Second thoughts – this is my projection of what I would like them to have, not what they want – so think again!) Also, a day out with their Dad to see a Rugby match in the near future should go down well!

Now, the secret of losing weight is here in this diary, it's quite a revelation and the commercial world of diets will disagree with it. But it's quite simple really. Read on!

THOUGHT FOR THE DAY
What is the true meaning of Christmas?

24.12.2005   Day 93 Christmas Eve

What's it all about?
Have we got enough?
Who do we have to buy for?
This year's going to be tough
Why do we do so much more?
I'll be glad when it's all over
What's on telly? Oh, my belly?
But, what's it all about?

Each of us have the special thought at Christmas.
One we keep to ourselves.
One that is deep, cherished and personal.
One that is touched on in quiet moments, in church, during silent night or even amongst the chatter of friends and relatives.
One that sets us apart from everyone else.
One that makes us unique and special.
You are infinitely valuable therefore, so am I says my friend.
So what's Christmas really about?

>   ***THOUGHT FOR THE DAY***
>   **Silent Night, Holy Night, Peace in Ourselves.**

25.12.2005   Day 94 Christmas Day

A Yorkshire Christmas (best said in a broad Yorkshire accent)

Ey up lad what's up wi thee?

Am frozen t deeth cant the see?

Ay put wood in hole then and sit thee sen down
Here, get this down ya neck it'll tek away frown
So, where's tha bin since I saw thee

I ve bin with sheep an shepherds over yonder by big tree

I say lad has tha seen yon star up loft

Nay, but three strange fellas came by with some rart lookin toft
They said a lad called Jesus was born tday

Ay tha knows, out back int barn it lay
By gum I rart goin on
Some little mite I'd say, mardy and sounding out of fettle
I said I'll git tea on and put on kettle

Then shepherds, kings, ox and ass all cum round
I said theres nowt but tea, but were drawn to sound
Then a good lookin lass, came over as I was stokin coal
And then she whispered in me luggole

Has tha got puddins in,
It might help bairn mek less din

So off I went to cook up mix
And echy thump they all got stuck in and gave it rart big licks
Contentment I say, there's
Nowt as good as a Yorkshire on Christmas day.

A Prayer for Christmas

At peace with myself
At peace with my family
At peace with my friends
At peace
Recognise that joy is in me and you
Recognise that pain is part of life
Recognise life is precious
Recognise me and you
Are things meant to be
Or can we influence for the better
Can we all join in one spirit and live together in harmony

Love me, love another
Respect, don't judge, raise the standard
I am infinitely valuable, therefore so are you
Stop the killing and blaming,
Forgive them and forgive myself
Work together to fight disease and famine
Look after our children they are our future
Look after our elders they are our wisdom
Look after our earth, it is our legacy
Look after each other for this is our hope
A new millennium, an old prayer
A new vision, a new hope
Together one community we can win over
And build that critical mass of belief
That the potential is there for humanity to be truly beautiful
This I pray for, for all our sakes

> ## *THOUGHT FOR THE DAY*
> **Eat less, drink less, be merry by really listening to those who you love and let the joy in your heart show.**

26.12.2005   Day 95 Boxing Day

The anniversary of the death of 250,000 poor souls in the path of a wave of ocean, lifted by the sea floor cracking hundreds of miles long, metres high – the wave then travelling at 500 miles an hour, and as it approaches the shore, builds up to 150 metres high to swallow up whole communities. These communities are now rebuilding their lives with courage and aid from all over the world.

Are we prepared for the next Tsunami? Predicted to occur off the West Coast of America. Can we ever be prepared when the power of our planet bites back?

Yesterday was great. Traditional over-indulgence in food and gifts, but all in the context of giving and sharing with your loved ones. We contacted everyone in the family and many of our friends too. Now, today the rest of the family raid our hospitality – party time!

The Pope's Christmas message is a prayer for peace in Israel, our Head of The Church of England's message is forgiveness, and our Queen's message is a sober reflection of disaster and terrorism and the need for courage and hope.

My message this Christmas is related to all these, but it's one I give with a sense of dread, because I feel this time of year has yet to see its destructiveness and hope that it can change.

An Appeal to all those who wish to die for their cause
There is a more powerful and effective form of human expression.
It requires greater courage than suicide.
The effect lasts longer and it opens the way to meaningful dialogue and peace.
To some, the thought of it is sickening – breaking through this nauseous barrier can result in sensing a new freedom of the human spirit.
It doesn't require an understanding, appreciation or acceptance of the others' situation or beliefs – just an acknowledgement that there will always be history and differences – this will not change.
What can change is ones own sense of personal value and the desire for your family and community to live and enjoy the wisdom that comes with growing old together.
Some say it's war! Yet war is the consequence of any leader's inability to communicate and compromise, with one or both sides assuming a divine right over the other.
Dying for ones cause may seem a glorious act and some believe a way out into a better life.
Yet doesn't it mean that no matter how many take this path of 'glorious suicide' there will always be many more who don't, left behind in treacherous conflict and a severe poverty of happiness.
Surely there is another way?
There is.
It's called
FORGIVENESS.

OK, I dare you to do the following exercise. Write down everything you drank and ate on Christmas Day – here's my list:

- Bacon and egg sandwich
- 1 glass of Bucks Fizz
- 1 glass of Champagne
- 2 pints of lager
- ¾ bottle of red wine
- Turkey and Cranberry Sauce and stuffing
- Parsnips
- Broccoli
- Carrots & Swede
- Leeks in a Cheese Sauce
- Onion gravy
- Cheese and biscuits
- Whisky and coke
- 1 pint of lager
- 1 glass of white wine
- A yogurt
- 1 ham sandwich
- 2 turkey sandwiches

Quite a lot, but better than last year! What's missing here is – no crisps, nuts, chocolate, trifle, pudding, potatoes and sausage. I know – I'm kidding myself – still, hope I don't put on too much and the exercise is going well!

27.12.2005   Day 96

This mornings' sunshine glistening and dancing off a layer of crisp brilliant white snow is a wondrous sight. It's good to be alive!

THOUGHT FOR THE DAY
Look deep and long enough and you can see the beauty in most things.

28.12.2005　Day 97

My body is telling me something. My indigestion system is shouting at me. It's saying – stop! Too Much!! Enough is enough, please no more excess, 2 days of over the top eating and drinking – back to moderation.

M　meaningful eating, ask yourself, why are you eating this right now?
O　often and small meals rather than One Over large meal
D　decide to be healthy
E　exercise more and eat when you're hungry, not when you're emotional
R　respect yourself
A　accept it's your problem
T　time is now, no regrets or what ifs.....
I　invite answers to the questions who are you and what do you want?
O　occasional treats
N　never give up

The hills are calling – let's go!!

THOUGHT FOR THE DAY
Why is it that seeking pleasure often results in the abuse and destruction of our body?

29.12.2005　Day 98

Within 1½ hours we can be in the middle of some of the most beautiful countryside in the UK. We drove to its heart. A small village called Grassington in the Yorkshire Dales. Rarely will we experience such a perfect day. This day involved:-

· walking through ancient woods and seeing the fairy dust sparkle in the sunlight through wispy trees
· looking down on a raging river rolling beneath us and seeing it transform into a winding, meandering smooth water way

- feeling the cold air, breathing its freshness and knowing it was just below freezing, yet feeling warm and nourished inside, and the sun on our face
- slipping on the ice – dicing with danger
- pausing in a field of bulls – feeling intimidated but finding the courage to walk through
- looking above, seeing the white trails of the planes contrasted against bright blue sky – travelling to warmer climates
- climbing up steep hills, slippery slopes and squeezing through narrow styles
- rolling hills and majestic views sparkling in its daze with white majesty
- the comradeship of fellow walkers
- the sound of the birds, the occasional sheep, the rapids of the river and crunch of the snow
- the burning hills silhouetted in the dusk sky as the sun dips in its red glory
- tea and cake in a quaint tea shop in the village
- 9½ miles in 4½ hours

All the above is freely available to all those fit enough to experience it.

THOUGHT FOR THE DAY
Lose weight, gain freedom and drink in the beauty around you.

30.12.2005   Day 99

Elton John got married last week. Gay marriage has been a major news item all last week as the law has just been changed to allow a civil ceremony to take place so a legal partnership between gays can be recognised. This is good news in my opinion. There has always been and will always be people who prefer to be with their own gender – I believe from birth most of us are destined to express our sexuality in a certain way and for too long, homosexuality has been suppressed, stigmatised with great prejudice, causing misery to one in ten of the population.

It's important to feel free and comfortable to express yourself sexually. This will happen more easily if you are comfortable and at ease with your own body. The more attractive you think you are, the more attractive you will be to others, especially if it's conveyed with a sense of ease and confidence in who you are.

Being free in our loving relationships enables the free flow of giving and receiving energy. However, many people are hooked into relationships where access to loving energy is limited between themselves because of dependency. When initial attraction takes place, it's important to recognise that on one hand this could be the start of a beautiful relationship where two complete people meet on equal terms, or it could be two incomplete people searching for answers in the other, which can often result in power struggles about who is dominant or in control.

The journey of two people in true partnership is a wonderful thing. To have it publicly recognised is icing on the cake. The important thing is the discovery of true love between two people. I have only been in love three times in my life. My first wife for 15 years was, I believe, a comfortable loving relationship, however, somehow, we both became depressed within it and something had to give before we both drowned.

A brief affair is my second love – the 'brief affair' description doesn't do it justice as it nearly changed the whole course of my life and career.

Which, in hindsight I'm glad it didn't as now I am with the love of my life.

A moment of love

Two flowers in the night
Wake and meet
Petals fall and thrill when
The silkiness of difference enjoy each others touch

Two flowers in the day
Jointly turn to the sun
Basking in the nourishment and rays of fun
Then buds move closer

Two flowers in the night
Touch and entwine
Their roots mingle
And each other becomes mine

Two flowers in the dawn
Wake and separate
Their bodies stronger and true
Their buds turn and sway to natures tune
to the music of knowing the joining of beauty

THOUGHT FOR THE DAY
What is love but the free giving and receiving with acceptance of who each of you are?

31.12.2005   Day 100 New Years Eve

The last day of 2005. What a year!

The Tsunami, the Pakistani Earthquake, New Orleans flooded, Cancun flattened, more African famine, Aids on the increase.

Terrorist bombings in London, kidnapping and murdering of hostages in Iraq, car bombs and suicide killings, other terrorist bombings in Egypt and Delhi.

Death of Pope John Paul, death of George Best, my friend Cliff about to die.

Our home in Florida – stolen – we are victims of fraud.

Our home in York developed – new garden and new conservatory.

Work steady, plus appointed as a non executive director.

Work trips and holidays include Florida twice, Spain, Tenerife, Barcelona, Warsaw, Hong Kong. Sister moves to Spain, most of family well.

Me – well it feels like new beginnings. A new sense of who I am. My loss of weight has been very gradual and this is the longest and most sustained period of focus and commitment to do so.

This is accompanied by a greater sense of who I am and what I am here to do and what I want in my life.

Woke up this morning with a sense of Cliff dead. No news yet, but I don't feel him here any longer. This is it, there is nothing else, just this. Here today, gone tomorrow – so what do we make of it?

01.01.2006   Day 101 New Years Day

New beginning, fresh start – increased resolve. Now it's putting everything described and all the insights in this diary into practice – watch the weight drop off! Stay off the booze for a while, give the liver a chance to recover! No snacks, small meals, eat only when hungry, keep up the exercise – simple – just do it!

02.01.2006   Day 102

If you look back and re-read this diary, and pick out the hints and tips for weight control, eating and drinking reduction etc – there's probably about a dozen things that can help. At the core of it all, however, there must be a real sense of its importance, a real acknowledgement that if you don't lose weight, then you will have sooner or later a serious problem with your health.

Combine this acknowledgment and commitment with a reminder of what you want as alternatives – ie, for me, longer fitter life, pain free joints, more golf and time with my wife and to take my Grandchildren to Disney – then we have a basis for moving forward.

The formula: no snacks, eat only when hungry, light meals and exercise is a sound basis for a sensible eating pattern. Some may, in addition, find writing down everything and estimating the calorie content is useful so that the total doesn't exceed for men, 2000 calories a day. However, I feel calorie counting is a small part of a fundamental resolve to get fit.

Drinking plenty of water and eating fruit and vegetables (at least 5 portions a day) will also help.

So, back on track after the Christmas and New Year excess. I've avoided weighing myself because I know, in myself, I have put on a few pounds, so – next WID on Saturday morning – let's see if we can get to the pre Christmas weight of 220lbs!

THOUGHT FOR THE DAY
Take less in and lighten up!

03.01.2006   Day 103

My friend Cliff lost his personal 'Battle of Hastings' this morning, 0920hrs.

THOUGHT FOR THE DAY
Rest in Peace, my friend.

04.01.2006   Day 104

Where is all this going? What's the point? Not untypical questions when experiencing loss of a loved one. Asking fundamental questions of one's own worth and purpose, and reflecting on life and death are valuable points of reflections.

I don't think I fear death itself, however, I have some increased anxiety about the 'process' of dying, having witnessed my friend die a slow and uncomfortable death. At these times, it's difficult to make the ordinary things in life important.

Getting back to work, making those calls, responding to e-mails all seems insignificant.

Yet, as they say, life goes on and one does not have to look very far to find inspiration. The families and emergency services of 9/11, the survivors of the Tsunami and Pakistan earthquake all help to put these things in perspective.

Every moment of everyday, I have to keep reminding myself of my personal power. The power to choose, to choose how to be. Also, to recognise that every action I have will have an effect and better for that effect to have a conscious purpose. What is this conscious purpose? For me, it's about creating benefit, help and good for others – granted, I fall down some of the time and indulge in seemingly bland meaningless activity, like habitually watching TV or engaging without listening! But, if I apply this 'choice and purpose' principle to my life in every moment, I can choose to be purposeful. I can choose to be happy or sad, I can choose to eat or not eat – the power is mine.

THOUGHT FOR THE DAY
What choices as I going to make today and why?

05.01 and 06.01.2006   Days 105 / 106

Our dear friend from Scotland is staying with us for a few days. He is a student at Edinburgh University. As a student he is a member of a small charity that focuses its contributions to a project each year in a village in Africa – last year, they built a school, this year, they built a bridge. The bridge meant an essential journey to have their maize ground was cut down from a 37 hour trek to a 2 hour trek. We like to contribute a little each time to purchase something to help improve self sufficiency in the village. This year, we bought a Yenga Press which helped them press rape seed locally instead of travelling and having to pay for it to be pressed. Part of the agreement involved them contributing any profits made to the school. We have pictures and a video of all this going on so it's good to see how ones contribution is being used directly and to be thanked personally by the people concerned. We can only do this, of course, as long as we have someone courageous enough to live and work with the villagers to see the project through – thanks George.

Multiply this event by 1 million and a global change in the economy will be for the better. Hey, but we have to start somewhere.

Weight – put on 4lbs, not surprised – I know what to do!

THOUGHT FOR THE DAY
A liver is for life, not just for Christmas.

07.01.2006   Day 107

I can't put my fingers on this, but I sense something is shifting in World politics, climate or something significant is about to happen. Ariel Sharon, the Israeli Prime Minister is critically ill after a stroke and several brain surgical operations.

Charles Kennedy, our Liberal Democrat leader, has resigned – part pressure but hopefully, part realisation he needs to take care of himself.

The last two days, we have explored with our friends the politics of charity in Africa. Our sponsored child in Africa has moved. We got a letter from our new child sponsor.

Friends of ours are cycling in south west China and texting us about the poverty and primitive conditions, and the fear of bird flu mutation. Turkey is culling its chickens as 4 people die of bird flu.

I watch again the film about Mahatma Ghandi. It seems too quiet over the pond – so what's the Bush administration up to?

My dreams lately have been quite vivid related to life and death issues – not surprising given the recent death of my friend, but I sense they are telling me something else. We have just booked our holiday for South Africa in November, and I turn the TV on – the film Zulu Dawn is ending – the great battle and turning point where British rule starts to end in Africa.

So, are all these events just random incidents that I just connect in some way, or is there something else going on?

I believe we are all in some way connected. The more in tune with ourselves the more aware we become of these connections. I sense a shift in me and the World. Change is inevitable.

Change begins and is constant throughout my life.
Understanding myself throughout change is my desire, yet so hard to do.
To accept my own personal pain as a gift and to recognise my own potential for learning during these times is a challenge, but worthy of celebration.
Letting go of the past and changing myself through the unknown risks being lost and, therefore, I can only rely on myself as the guide, this is my hope.

Being conscious in every moment and being aware and responsible for my influence reminds me of my power.

Taking care of myself and being open to receiving creates opportunities for me to give.

I need to learn in order to change, being present and connecting this awareness to my desires for the future will enable me to move.

I can thrive on change and the change of others, for within this learning partnership I can see my worth and the worth of others.

My thirst for knowledge will surround me with books and help me strive for new experiences so I can listen and grow.

I value my tears as I know they are a path to joy.

I strive to listen more to my body so it doesn't have to shout so much.

I pray that what I write becomes real and that I live with a trust that gives me peace.

(published in Managing Change at Work by Mike Wash, Published by MB2000)

THOUGHT FOR THE DAY
Change or die.

08.01.2006   Day 108

I believe our bodies are a reflection of our experience of the world. I am overweight because I carry so much baggage – grief, guilt, self doubt, low self esteem, sadness etc etc – are all part of me that I wear from time to time. Over the years, these scars have been covered up by layers of comfort eating, hence the shape I am today.

To lighten up, I need to release myself from this baggage – which through this process of honest reflection and record, I am.

The mind and body is one and together they form a unique system of energy and information – hence our bodies are a product of our awareness.

I read somewhere (After Deepak Chopra, Ageless Body, Timeless Mind) that to stay young and fit, you need to have the following in your life:-

(1 = not present, 5 = very present and successful)
My rating:

5 Happy marriage (or partnership)
4 Job satisfaction
4 Feeling of personal happiness
4 Ability to laugh freely and easily
4 Satisfactory sex life
3 Ability to make and keep close friends
4 Regular daily routine
3 Regular work routine
5 Taking regular holidays
5 Feeling in control of personal life
4 Enjoyable leisure time, satisfying hobbies
4 Ability to express feelings easily
4 Optimism about the future
4 Financially secure, living within means
5 A sense of belief about who you are and what your purpose
   is
3 Feeling physically healthy and fit

If you score 50 or below, then you are probably perceived as unhappy. My score, at the moment, is 64 – happy!

I found the following poem amongst my Aunties old papers (she is now deceased – my Aunty, the Doyle Carte Opera Singer, who died of Multiple Sclerosis)

In Search of Happiness

Looking here, looking there,
Nothing and no one can tell where
I have been searching a long time
Perhaps the tale can be found in rhyme
Happiness, it must be sought
Never, never can it be bought
Though it's whereabouts be known
There is only one way to find happiness alone
That is to share all you love for one

To give an unselfish gift
And see a sad heart lift

Only you can make it true
When the right time comes shining through
So don't try to manufacture bliss
With an untrue word or silly kiss
You will only find it deep in your heart
And if it is real it will never depart
From a genuine soul and God given heart.

Enid Nicholson (aka Betty Wash)

THOUGHT FOR THE DAY
What will lift my heart and make me laugh today?

09.01.2006   Day 109

We sorted out and planned our breaks for the year yesterday. This is important because if we don't make them a priority and plan work around them, then before you know it – work has taken over. At the moment, we haven't secured enough work to comfortably afford these breaks – but I am confident it will come.

Taking time out, exploring new places, meeting new people, playing golf or doing your favourite things, having time for reflection and exercise are all vital elements to nourish the body and soul. The ultimate is to have this lifestyle intertwined on a daily or regular basis. The trap is to work even harder knowing you have a break planned – and then spend half the break de-stressing. You just begin to unwind and get into the holiday, and then it's time to go back to work!

I left that routine behind some years ago, but I do know of many others who struggle to balance life and work. Work is a means to an end (not the other way round). Having some idea of what that 'end' looks like can help reinforce the need for balance now. Usually, end of work life – people want to enjoy themselves. To do this, they have to be fit. Stress is one of the major causes of illness. It's connected to heart disease and cancer.

So often, people are trapped in a cycle of my work is important, I am important, I have to keep up appearances and be seen to be successful, this involves working harder than most, because what I do is important. This may all be true – but at what cost?

Then there are those who are addicted to work. This addiction develops over years and is partly delusional. What I mean by this is that the individual feels that the business, or team or country, can't be as successful without them. They forget how easy it is to replace them. They take on the identity of the position and everything revolves around this 'ego', this persona of status and importance. Prime Ministers, Presidents, government representatives, celebrities and senior executives come to mind. Get a life I say – get real. Don't lose the common touch, don't forget how much we are all alike and part of the same family.

THOUGHT FOR THE DAY
Be still not busy, be quiet not loud.

10.01.2006   Day 110

Reflecting on yesterdays sentiments links to my thoughts on leadership.

Do you care about others
Are you willing to give them time
Can you get angry about the failure
And waste caused by crime?

Do you have a passion to make a difference
Can you help others see another option
Are you prepared to make a stance
And communicate clearly your position
Standing boldly stating what's possible
And excite those around you,
Who in turn you inspire
To work beyond the ordinary
With passion, zeal and fire.

Can people read you and your values
Know what you stand for
See your bold and good intent
So they can rely on your candour.

Do you seek out opportunities to learn
From your own and indeed others mistakes
Thriving on new knowledge and yearn
For the opportunity to release the brakes
On people's potential so they can grow
From the seeds you sow.
Can you cry about other's pain
Shout about injustice
Guard against false fame
And listen carefully in case you miss
The wisdom of others.

Do you put into practice
Those values you hold dearly
Those principles you preach
Those behaviours you desire
And those standards you hope to reach.

Can you reflect on your day
And admit to learn
That maybe another way
May lead you to earn
The respect of others who say
We have ideas too
If you let us follow through
And do
For you and us
To
Achieve extraordinary things
That reflect the spirit and pride
You often hide
Until the applause and roar
Of success are so evident
You may as well sit back and enjoy the ride.

Leaders are big, leaders are small
Leaders don't always walk tall
Quite often they talk with their actions
Quite often they speak with knowledge
And confidence that within a fraction
They can and will take themselves to the edge
Of the unknown to achieve that bit extra
So others benefit and learn
From the legacy of a unique contribution
That makes a difference.

If deep down, these qualities highlighted here
Stir with recognition and instil
That sense of purpose to be true
To an ideal and way of being
Then yes,
Perhaps this is you

(Published in Managing Change at Work by Mike Wash, published by MB2000)

THOUGHT FOR THE DAY
Leaders are fat, leaders are thin – but better to lead from within.

11.01.2006 Day 111

Our government has just launched it's 'RESPECT' programme. This is a push on decreasing 'yobbish' behaviour, reducing muggings, street violence, graffiti, burning cars etc. Giving more power to communities to hold police to account, more attention to parent education and accountability. It's about time, but I feel it's too little, too late. The opposition government are talking about some form of conscripted service after leaving school. There may be something in this although I suspect many social / behavioural problems are with children before they end school, so more imaginative schooling activity probably needs to happen. I suspect many of those who hang around on streets find themselves involved in drugs or violent related incidents are not otherwise gainfully employed. I believe there is something about learning to appreciate work, working with others, the satisfaction of doing a good job and the value of a wage – all helping contribute to behaviour acceptable to society. For me, between the ages of 15 and 18, during school holidays, weekends and before I started my full-time career, I remember doing the following jobs: delivering milk, serving and stocking in a grocer shop, cleaning print machines with oil cloth, store keeping print roles, cleaning a warehouse floor every morning, packing bread, steam cleaning bread boards, feeding a milk bottle cleaning machine, loading milk vans, delivering furniture, demolishing old buildings – all these jobs, I remember doing with pride in the knowledge I will get my own money. Some of which, I gave to my mother, but I had more than enough to spend on enjoying myself at the time. I certainly don't remember hanging about on street corners – I was often too tired to do that and had a 7.30am start for work in the morning.

The answer lies somewhere between adequate policing, responsive communities, education, parenting, schools and alternative activity options, increasing the level of self respect in our youth today.

Our society, over the last 10 years, certainly has taken a turn for the worse in terms of 'dangerous streets' and 'no go areas' – it's time to transform these communities.

Looking back over my early work years – there was something satisfying about doing a physical job. The tiredness was a healthy tiredness, whereas a 'desk job' can give you a 'stressful' tiredness. This is why exercise is so important for me. I am now doing 30 minutes on my cross trainer at least 5 times a week. It feels good afterwards and I am sure is helping all round fitness.

THOUGHT FOR THE DAY
Respecting yourself will help you respect others.

12.01.2006   Day 112

How does one become light hearted, carefree, joyous and fun? It's mid-winter and approaching the anniversary of my sisters' death. For years I have, at this time of year, wrestled at best with a melancholic air about me, at worst – depression. I am confident this year will be different.

Partly because I feel stronger in myself and because we will be distracted in Portugal with friends and golf!

Sunshine does, I believe, have an effect on your disposition. This last week, we have seen perhaps 1 hour of sunshine – most of the time, it has been dark, dreary and damp. We have been indoors most of the time and watched hours of TV. If we were in Florida – we would be out!

So, this time of year for me means I have to make a special effort to lighten up – it's so easy for my grief to be triggered.

This is particularly difficult now as my friend Cliff's funeral is next Tuesday and the family have asked me to say a few words! Maybe I should add this to my list of 'roles' – the funeral speaker!

It's important to keep the 'black dog' (as Sir Winston Churchill called it) at bay by not allowing the weather, anniversary or past grief get in the way of what I want to be. I believe there is more to becoming light hearted, care free and fun than just avoiding depressing things.

Light hearted will also help with being light.

When I am depressed or melancholic, I will eat and drink, so it's even more crucial to keep on the path of 'enlightenment'.

I once went on a workshop where the facilitators decided we were a bunch of miserable souls and demanded that we laughed. We started to giggle, then laugh, then we couldn't stop – I am not sure what we were laughing at, but my sides hurt and my tears fell – it felt so good.

Seeing the funny side of life, not taking yourself and others too seriously sometimes helps release tension and gets us back to what really is important. I need to get better at this.

I have great difficulty in telling jokes for example. Maybe I should try more often. Let's set a goal today – to laugh with someone and to make someone laugh.

THOUGHT FOR THE DAY
Lighten up!

30.01.2006　　Day 113

Loss of 4lbs. Now we're talking! Achieved by being sensible. Let's keep it up!

Over 345 people were crushed to death on the pilgrimage in Mina, Saudi Arabia. During the ritual of stoning the wall, a surge meant many dying underfoot and hundreds were injured. Performance of the Hajj (pilgrimage to Mecca) is required of every Muslim who is financially and physically able to do so at least once in their lifetime. Millions of Muslims from all over the world make this 5 day religious journey every year.

This pilgrimage is a central part to the Muslim religion. When one has completed the journey, they return spiritually refreshed, forgiven of their sins and ready to start life anew, with a clean slate. Those who have performed the Hajj are often called by an honorary title 'Hajji' (one who has performed the Hajj).

Clearly, a major event in ones lifetime, and one not without risk.

To cater for and control millions at a time visiting one site is a major problem for the Saudi authorities – as I suspect over the years with the cost of travel and the wealth of nations all making it more possible to visit this holy city on the celebrated days in question. My thoughts and prayers are with those who have died and their grieving families.

We have our pilgrimages too – nothing on this scale and nothing tied into it being essential for atonement. Many journey to Rome, Lourdes and other holy sites – all seeking answers and healing of sorts. I believe rituals and symbols can help us focus on core values and principles of being good people. I wear a crucifix – a symbol of Jesus Christ. It reminds of a number of things – the brutality of humans, the courage of humanity, the ability to forgive. I see this each morning and sometimes my heart races with joy, and sometimes I become sombre – whatever is real at the time. This symbol brings out the essence of life and death for me – it helps me be real.

THOUGHT FOR THE DAY
What does being real mean today?

14.01 and 15.01.2006   Day 114 / 115

The Americans have just destroyed part of a village in Pakistan, killing 15 villagers, claiming to have killed one of Al Qaeda's leaders. When will this killing end?

Will we ever be able to live peacefully side by side?

No matter how many leaders are killed, how much anti-terrorist activity, spy and intelligence network, policing and protection action – there will always be someone willing to die for their cause and take others with them.

The United Nations are now considering sanctions against Iran because they have renewed their Nuclear Power programme. There is an anxiety throughout most of the World that they will eventually develop nuclear arms. A weapon in the hands of a regime which apparently despises the west and in particular, Israel, seems to be dangerous – so must be stopped. How? Please, god, let's talk. Please God, let our Nations understand each other better.

The answer has to be forgiveness and compromise on all sides. This can only be done by an honest dialogue with all concerned. Can we design an 'Amnesty Forum' where this could occur? A virtual peace conference where everyone who believes that they have a cause or a claim or a need for justice or a need to minimise war come together and put their requests on the table. For every request, there must be a 'give'. We can dream, hope and pray!

THOUGHT FOR THE DAY
What does it take to become a leader of peace?

16.01, 17.01 and 18.01.2006   Day 116, 117 and 118

Strange few days. Feels a little like a pilgrimage. Journey down to Margate to see Aunty Lil, an 80 year old gem. Mave's mum's sister – and still very Italian. An award winning opera singer who still sings in concerts to entertain the old folk! We stayed one night with her. She used to run a large hotel in Margate with her husband, now deceased. She treats her guests as 5 star guests. The house is immaculate, pristine, everything in its place – as it has been since her husband died 12 years ago. Our bed sheets are aired and dusted with a slight smell of lavender, towels in the bathroom are mysteriously replaced if you use them just once. She is a lively lady who gets angry and irritated at getting old, who is fiercely independent but frightened of walking out on her own sometimes as she feels threatened by what she perceives as 'foreigners' flooding into Margate, unable to find work but receiving benefit.

She tells us she doesn't want to live longer than she is able to look after herself. Saying goodbye is always emotional.

We move on to Hastings – the site of the battle everyone remembers – 1066 – and the site of my friend Cliff's last battle.

The service was a Catholic Mass – the church was suitably full, the tears flowed as his coffin was brought in. Cliff's partner and family had asked me to say a few words. I paid tribute to a great man with a great heart. He was buried on a sloping valley, looking at hills all around him.

Too much emotion, too much drink, too much food, too much driving, too much.

THOUGHT FOR THE DAY
What is just enough?

19.01.2006   Day 119

This time of year – everyone seems to be on a diet! There's plenty to choose from – here is a small selection of diets of our time!

Cabbage Soup Diet
> Eat as much soup made of cabbage, onion and tomato as you like. Stand back and wait for the explosion!

Chocolate Diet
> Just eat pasta, popcorn and chocolate, oh, and some fruit and veg.

Atkins Diet
> High protein, low carbohydrate. One for those who like meat, cheese, eggs and happy to forget fruit, pasta and potatoes. Works by encouraging ketoses, which suppresses the appetite.

Watch out for bad breath, constipation and possible kidney problems long term.

7 Day All-You-Can Eat Diet
First four days – fruit and veg only then chicken or beef and veg.

Chicken Soup Diet
Breakfast and chicken soup only (recipe involves lots of veg!)

Slimfast
Milkshakes and one meal a day!

Mayo Diet
Grapefruit, eggs, steak, cabbage and mayonnaise seem to be the main ingredients.

Caveman Diet
Mainly meat, fruit and veg – no bread or pasta – eat like the wild men used to!

Zone Diet
Maintaining the correct proportion of carbohydrates, protein and fat.

The Blood-Type Diet
Plenty of fruit and veg, but special foods for certain blood types.

Prifkin Diet
Very low fat intake.

Grapefruit Diet
Grapefruit with every meal (apparently, it contains a fat burning enzyme).

South Beach Diet
A version of a low carbohydrate diet.

Raw Food Diet
Basically – raw vegetables!

The list is endless – I counted over 300 on the internet. It's quite easy to promote your own – this is mine. I will call it – My Favourite Meal Diet.

Breakfast   Grapefruit and Cereal

Lunch   Fruit and / or salad

Favourite Meal (Add Vegetables)

Chicken Curry / Fish and Chips / Lasagne / Steak or just have your favourite meal for dinner with 2 glasses of Red Wine.

See this as a reward for discipline during the day.

Combine this with 30 minutes of aerobic exercise, 5 times a week + 4 pints of water a day and watch the weight come off.

Of course – it's all a load of rubbish. Why these diets work initially is because you do start to reduce your calorific intake, eat less, change your metabolism. But it is all short term and the vast majority of people will put the weight back on.

Weight loss and maintenance has to be long term, integrated into a permanent way of behaviour based on the belief and value that:

    a   you have the choice
    b   health is the most important thing in your life
    c   you want to be happy

THOUGHT FOR THE DAY
My friend in Africa, after he had explained the next stage of the bridge building project to a group of villages, asked if any one had any questions. An elderly man stood up and said "Yes – how did you get so fat?"

20.01.2006   Day 120

What a mixed up, confused society we are. The government, having reconsidered the classification of cannabis, decided to leave it in the lesser serious drug group. That's the message – despite growing evidence of its dangers. Re-classifying it probably won't make much difference to its use and abuse, what does, and has made a difference – is to publicise its dangers. I remember as a young mental health nurse admitting young men with schizophrenia and depression – this was in the 1970's. Was it just a coincidence that the vast majority of them had a history of smoking cannabis and taking LSD?

On most markets and in some specialist shops, you can buy hallucinogenic and mind altering weeds / herbs that are completely legal – but just as dangerous. We will never stop this trade, but I propose that we could do a lot more in education and advertising to inform people of the dangers.

I remember a friend of mine having smoked cannabis one night – he ended up running around the hospital grounds frightened to death someone was chasing him – and that was the mild stuff!!

Today's weed is ten times stronger. I can smell the weed a mile off – it remains strong with me because my sister was freely smoking it in her last 10 days of life at home. It can be comforting and relaxing and beneficial to people with certain long term illnesses, eg: multiple sclerosis – but come on – time we gave clear messages to our young society instead of mixed, confused messages!

Here's another howler – apparently, we have sex offenders working in our schools with our children! Some bright ministers approved a number of appeals to work from teachers, who have been prosecuted for having child pornography or some related offence. Now, I ask you – would you leave a diabetic child who is hungry in a room full of sweets?

Why would a convicted sex offender want to continue working with children? As a parent, would you be comfortable knowing that, even if it was 20 or 30 years ago – your child's teacher was found to be erotically stimulated by child pornography – come on!!! It's a no brainer.

So, after weeks of protest and cases highlighted, the government has decided – no one on the sex offenders list should teach – and a panel of experts, not ministers, should be the guardians of the list. By the way – apparently we have 5000 teachers from overseas – who vets them?

I think what's missing in government today is what I would call a 'common sense scrutiny committee'.

By the way – our Florida Home saga – Jeb Bush, the governors office reply? Not our jurisdiction / concern!!

Attorney General's Office? No response apart from 'we are dealing with it'.

Governors Office for Notary Complaint? All our material and evidence returned because they had moved office (in the same building) but 'haven't changed their address on the internet yet'.

Out Attorney? No response for over 2 weeks, despite many emails and messages.

It doesn't bode well!

However – lost another 2lbs – so, not all bad! (218lbs / 15 stone, 8 lbs).

THOUGHT FOR THE DAY
My past may not have caused me to be fat – but it may be keeping me fat. Let it go!

21.01.2006   Day 121

We have bought a few Euro-Lottery tickets – the prize is a record draw of £8.5 Million. What on earth would we do with this? Good Question.

I would find a suitable small region of poverty in the world and invest in a regeneration project. Probably Africa.

I would invite my friends, whom also happen to be very creative organisational development consultants, to run the project.

The would include George, the 2 Grahams, Lindsey, Colin, Basil, Helen and Marina.

Mave and I would oversee the project – do a quality review to see how it's going (and communicate the lesson learned throughout the world). This, of course, would be in between, our travels all over the world, learning, enjoying the experience and dropping seeds of development to encourage peace and reduce poverty wherever we go.

I may have an indulgence or two, like a place in Naples, Florida with my boat moored at the bottom of the garden. Of course, we would look after the family – Myles – top of the range BMW, Philippa – house of her dreams, Matt and Tom – Golf Course, Matt could run the bar and restaurant, Tom the pro-shop. Kirsty – a little Bistro in Portugal. The rest – pay off their debts.

Would all this make us happy? Doubt it – probably cause more problems, tensions, upset, stress etc. Happiness can not be bought.

22.01.2006   Day 122

One of the significant contributors to being overweight is, I believe, due to distorted beliefs.

These distorted beliefs can be developed in childhood, or created due to some significant event in life. For me, it's both. Here are my distorted beliefs about food:-

- · If you don't eat everything on your plate – you are being disrespectful to the starving millions in the World.
- · You can't have a dessert unless you eat all your main meal.
- · The more I eat, the more proud my parents will be of me.
- · The more I eat, the stronger I will get.
- · I can always burn off excess if I overeat (can, but opportunities to eat excessively invariably outweigh burn off time)
- · Eating, somehow, will comfort me and help my emotions.
- · Eating everything and asking for more is paying a compliment to the cook.

And the big distortion, developed more recently than the others:

- · Why should I deprive myself of the things I enjoy now if I am going to die young of cancer anyway?

So, all of these have played a part in my behaviour and attitude to food. I wonder what your distorted beliefs are? Recognising them is the first step. Then, catching yourself in the moment when they are influencing your choice is the second. Then, choosing to eat without the distorted belief influencing is the way forward.

THOUGHT FOR THE DAY
Take the distortion out of your beliefs, take out your parents beliefs/influence (you can put them back later) then find out what you really believe.

23.01.2006   Day 123

We have just returned from a Pantomime Weekend. Our friend, who usually plays the Dame, this time excelled himself as the flying wicked witch in Snow White and the Seven Dwarfs. Good, clean, light hearted fun which every child enjoys and every adult enjoys being a child again.

Awful acting, great dancing, dreadful jokes, good singing, everyone in the audience shouting and participating – Oh yes they do, oh no they don't – he's behind you!

Our friend Paul is to Stevenage what Berwick Kaler is to York. Every year, every city, every town and village put on a pantomime when we all laugh at ourselves. A great custom. it's good not to take ourselves too seriously – rediscovering the free flowing fun and spontaneity of being a child is refreshing.

A whale has been lost in the Thames these last few days – a rescue attempt failed – it died. That's awful.

THOUGHT FOR THE DAY
Keep smiling and do something spontaneous.

24.01.2006   Day 124

I have spent sometime over the last week clearing out old photos, letters and mementoes and keeping things that may be precious for my children when I am gone. Sounds morbid, but it feels just part of the process of cleaning up, tidying, sorting out unfinished business. It's amazing how much clutter we accumulate over the years and it's good as part of the 'lightening up' process to clear out from time to time. This process can be quite therapeutic as re-reading old letters and looking at old photos can bring back significant events which you either need to re-enjoy or put in the bin forever.

THOUGHT FOR THE DAY
Don't put off til tomorrow what you can do or say today.

25.01.2006   Day 125

Sensible eating going well. Fatmea is under control. I can't let up though. I have to keep recognising the triggers to eating and those vulnerable moments. For example, when I am bored. I think – what's to eat?

After a tough or stressful day – I think – perhaps I'll have a drink which then weakens the resolve, so I eat more.

Watching less than interesting and entertaining TV – I think this would be more enjoyable if I was eating at the same time.

These are all times when it is so easy to sabotage myself. It's good to recognise and write down the times when you are vulnerable. Be more aware and take more personal choice in what you do in these circumstances. Find alternatives – move away or change the circumstances in which you feel vulnerable.

THOUGHT FOR THE DAY
Recognising and understanding your weaknesses and vulnerability can be a strength.

26.01.2006   Day 126

Occasionally, I will dig out my 'family tree' files and do a little more work on tracing my ancestors. A highlight so far was to discover that my Great, Great Uncle – George Walker Milburn (on my mother's side) was a famous sculptor. He sculpted the William Etty statue (a famous York artist) outside the York Art Museum, the Queen Victoria statue, now in Acomb Park, and the George Leeman statue outside York Railway Station. Also, he has 4 pieces in York Minster – one of them being King Edwin, another Edward VII – both magnificent pieces in the Choir Sanctuary.

His masons yard was by the side of Bootham Bar in York. Most of the Yorkshire Millburn's were tradesmen of sorts, some tailors and some leather workers living in the Shambles or Goodramgate. Half of my Grandfather's family in 1925 went to Australia on the SS Oriana, these were his 3 brothers, one of which had 10 children. On the Wash side – no strong claim to fame yet. Originally from around

Maidstone, Kent, Wash may refer to the land type 'bog dwellers – marshland' and / or there is a connection to Washington, USA on the coat of Arms (red stripes and stars) are very similar and go back to the c. 1200. My grandfather's brother emigrated to Canada in early 1900's and had a big family, and I am now in communication with my Canadian Cousins.

Most of the Wash's seem to come from strong labourer stock – hard working grafters!

THOUGHT FOR THE DAY
What legacy will I leave?

27.01.2006   Day 127

Well, here we are in Portugal! It's pouring down with rain, although a little warmer than the UK. We have a very simple agenda – to meet and catch up with old friends and play good golf. The latter being more of a challenge.

Playing any sport well takes practice, focus, discipline and fitness. To play extremely well takes you into how the mind affects performance. People talk about being in 'the zone' – I believe this exists. In golf, it has only ever happened to me once for 9 holes, when I was par up to 8 then one over on the 9th – I remember it was a hot summers day, a lot of flies around that didn't bother me – I almost saw them as my friends. My mind was empty and I just played. To play well, you have to have a sense of presence that totally gives yourself to the situation. Feel the earth, grass, trees, be part of the weather and visualise what you want to do. Relax, focus and enjoy. Avoid thinking about the external distractions of life, and don't put too much importance in scoring – concentrate on the being and the process then the results will come. As you sense, this theory of golf is also a theory of life.

THOUGHT FOR THE DAY
How do I move and be still at the same time?
(Loss of another 2lbs – good! (216lbs – 15 stone, 6 lbs)

28.01.2006   Day 128

So much for the theory of golf. We managed to get to the 14th before the elements of wind and rain had their day!! It rained almost continuously but despite our cheery disposition and determination - common sense prevailed! We did meet up with old friends which was our main objective and we had a wonderful meal with their family that evening.

Graham caught me moaning about the size of the hire car - a Volkswagen Golf - because the boot was too small to put a golf bag in! He said that I lived in a completely different world than VW Golf drivers! That challenge hooked me into the same 'guilt' trip as - not to leave food on my plate because of the starving millions in this world. My retort tried to be clever - 'oh, I thought everyone played golf'- but you do need to afford the clubs and green fees can be expensive. Since 90% of the worlds population live on less than $2 a day, of course - I shouldn't moan about the size of the car.

Does that mean I should be grateful for everything? Yes.

Does it mean I shouldn't moan? No, not necessarily. There is nothing wrong with seeking for better things, as long as this is not your purpose in life. Things are just things and are temporary, superficial and unimportant in the scheme of life. However.....

THOUGHT FOR THE DAY
When hiring a car in Portugal or Spain - check the boot size is big enough for golf clubs!!

29.01.2006   Day 129

Hamas, the militant political party in Palestine have just won their election. Israel are calling on the World to not recognise this government unless they reject terrorism. Suicide bombings have been a main weapon of this group. I hope and pray Hamas recognise they can achieve more through politics than through suicide, and a real dialogue of peace begins.

A derelict 17th Century Franciscan convent in the mountains overlooking Monchique town and valley, surrounded by cork trees and Satsuma under a bright blue sky and brilliant sunshine. Streams of spring water, mountain roads, roman spas, a donkey and pigeons that somersault in formation. A walk in the local town passing fish cooked outside on a barbeque and getting to know where we are.

A perfect day.

THOUGHT FOR THE DAY
What is perfection if it is not now, the moment we cherish?

30.01.2006   Day 130

Golf rained off! The sun shone just enough for us to walk around ancient Arabian fortress battlements in Silves. The evening was a wine fuelled event full of challenging conversation, cards and charades, as is the norm with our friends in Portugal.

Prayers and thoughts go to those who died and their families in the collapsed stadium in Poland. Over 65 people crushed after the roof fell in, apparently – under the weight of snow!

THOUGHT FOR THE DAY
What is friendship?

31.01.2006   Day 131

Yesterday was a perfect blue sky golf day – with less than perfect golf – but hey – who cares?!?

Today is the anniversary of my sisters' death. She died 31st January 1985, aged 25. For seven years, she struggled to survive through life with kidney failure.

For much of those years, she was on a kidney machine, yet this to her was only part of the struggle. Just as significant to her was her drive to discover truth – truth about herself, to know why and who she was. This journey took her down a path of self-destruction, only to emerge damaged and discovering many things about herself and life.

The following is a personal account of Veronica's death, a death that involved both pain and joy – indeed a real celebration.

At the age of 16, in January 1976, Veronica was to experience what I believe to be the most traumatic event in her life. She was in Singapore with our Mother, staying whilst my father worked out there. My mother fell from a balcony, suffering head injuries from which she would never recover. Veronica discovered her mother, lying injured after the fall. I don't believe Veronica ever came to terms with that picture of our poor mother. Our mother remained in hospital, not speaking, not moving and having to be fed by tube, helpless and still. She remained like this until she died on 31st March 1979.

17 months after our mothers' accident, Veronica was diagnosed as having renal failure. It was decided – because I was already training to be a general nurse, I could help maintain Veronica on a dialysis machine at home. This we did for two years, eventually, two other nurses and a friend and my older sister trained to help out, enabling me to focus on my newly formed family, Thomas and Matthew, born August 1978. Shortly after this, Veronica received a kidney transplant.

This transformed her life, freeing her. With this new found freedom, she made an attempt to make up for what she had missed. This included a trip to the Philippines with father. Unfortunately, she acquired a series of infections which started the rejection process of her kidney. She returned to the UK to be told she would have to resort to surviving with the help of a machine again.

To be placed on a kidney machine, two needles must be inserted into a large vein. The size of the vein can be enlarged by a simple operation of joining two veins together, the increased pressure increasing the size and thickness of the vein. This now had broken down, so a 'graft' had to be placed in her leg. Unfortunately, this became infected which led to the debate – does she live or die?

During many hours spent in a hospital bed, on what was in effect a 'life support machine', Veronica often took herself on a journey inwards. Many of these journeys were fantasy, themes of love and happiness, many were of confusion and questions, some were of torment and pain leading to severe bouts of depression.

To her, life on a machine was a different reality to most, her frustrations of being unable to relate to others experiencing a so called normal life was one of the factors that encouraged her towards relating to those who sought alternative reality through escape. She found solace, friendship, company and support in a circle of individuals who relied heavily on drugs. It was her use and abuse of drugs that eventually resulted in her situation of facing her death.

What you are about to read is my account of Veronica's last eleven days.

Sunday, Day 1

As we walked into the side room, we were immediately warned of the risk of Hepatitis – the vision immediately brought back the image of our mother, lying there, unconscious, head slightly back, the fan going, still.

My big sister was with me – Veronica, who is our baby sister, acknowledged us and said "I think I've had it this time, Mike".

"What do you mean?"

"I'm going to die."

Eventually, the story unfolded from how Veronica saw it – a serious infection in her 'graft' had broken down so they could not use it again – she needed a further operation to implant a graft in her leg – however, the medical team were reluctant to go ahead because of the risk (due to Hepatitis) for the surgeon and nursing team. Also, as far as Veronica's consultant was concerned, other factors relating to Veronica's lifestyle and attitude to life gave rise to the consideration whether or not to continue dialysis.

Veronica's consultant came into hospital from home especially to see us – I wasn't sure that what Veronica was saying was accurate or maybe I just didn't want to believe it. During the discussion, he seemed to be putting the decision on to the family. "No way" I said "The decision is yours and I'm not going to say anything that will make your decision easy!"

I was angry – surely there must be an alternative. What about peritoneal dialysis (through the abdomen)? He mumbled something about infective fluids for long periods of time – all I could think of was what Veronica wanted. If she wanted dialysis, then I would have found some way of providing it – but it wasn't to be – we went back to Veronica – she asked

"What did he say?"

"Not much more that what you told us, but he emphasised that it was a life and death issue."

"I've had enough Michael, I don't want this graft in my leg. I'm sick of sticking needles into me."

"What if I told you they were considering stopping dialysis anyway because of the risk and your situation?"

"Then that's OK" she said.

"But I don't want you to die" I cried.

My other sister says "I want you to be happy."

"Then let me die."

Monday, Day 2

Arriving at the hospital that afternoon, knowing what I must do, what I needed to say, desperate for time on my own with her.

The consultant met me, the issues – hard decisions, many involved ethical issues, potential news story – the need for everyone to be in one mind about what's going to happen. Veronica wants to die at home, then "Yes" I said – not realising or knowing what would happen – it didn't matter – it was imperative that Veronica got what she wanted.

I walked into her side room – my 3 other sisters were sat – they were all laughing – they greeted me affectionately. I responded superficially – not knowing what to say. I sat down. Arrangements needed to be made to take Veronica home. My sisters left. I was alone with Veronica – I broke down.

"I love you Ronk, I don't want you to leave me, let me do something to help."

"Oh, my big strong brother."

We hugged each other and cried a lot.

"You wouldn't be in this mess if I'd stayed by you, talked to you more, counselled you, prevented you taking drugs."

"You know that's not true – I would have done what I wanted to do – I always have – you couldn't have stopped me."

"Do you know what's going to happen?"

"I think an overdose of smack would do it."

"Do you really think that's the way?"

166

"No. How will I die?"

"As far as I know, the toxins will build up, you will become drowsy and confused, you won't be in pain and eventually will lapse into a coma."

"How long will the coma last?"

"24 to 48 hours."

"Oh, I don't want it to last more than 24 hours and I don't want to be in pain."

"I'll make sure you're alright."

"How long have I got?"

"May be 4 or 5 days."

"I want to sort my things out."

"Do you want to make a will?"

I wrote the will she dictated and a letter to Dad. We talked about how close we were, how much we loved each other and how much the distance this last year had effected us. She told me about her battle against heroin and how much she loved her boyfriend.

It was time to take her home. She went with my oldest sister, Barbara, and I left first, keen to get back to make sure everything was set up right for her. My other sisters and some friends were busy cleaning the house. Half an hour later, after I had arrived – Veronica came in. She had wanted to travel round York to see the Minster and some of her favourite places for the last time. The joy on her face was obvious to all as she came in and immediately she set about reassuring and consoling her boyfriend and three of her friends who were also waiting.

Barbara agreed to stay the first night. I reluctantly went home, to sleep maybe two or three hours. I was worried that her friends would tire her, and somehow prevent the family spending time with her – my anxiety peaked and wasn't to settle until Veronica reassured me the following morning.

Tuesday, Day 3

As I walked into the room she was sat up painting her nails – she looked 'well' – I sat by her. Told her how I felt, wanting time with her and knowing her family were wanting time – time they have missed over the last few years – she had given attention to her friends and vice versa and I said our needs were greater – God, how selfish I sound. Her reply was to the effect that she knew, she realised and there would be plenty of time for the family, she wanted her friends round her, especially when she was feeling OK, and if she was tired, she would just fall asleep anyway. I would know when she had had enough, and know what to do. My anxieties were not fully calmed until the night I was part of her 'celebration'.

She enjoyed the television on – every programme seemed significant, every word, she said, seemed so meaningful. She was pleased to know that Dad was on his way home. Her boyfriend seemed to be on the phone most of the day – the grapevine started – he seemed to be inviting hundreds round.

Our GP doctor visited. I could tell he wasn't happy or sure about the situation. It wasn't until two days later when he visited again and said "I feel so much love and strength here – it's really great – so, right – you're coping really well." He was reassured. I left again that night, knowing I would need my strength later on, and someone had to meet Dad off the plane at Leeds.

Wednesday, Day 4
I met Dad off the plane. I'm not sure how much he took in – he didn't cry much. It felt good having him home.

We entered the house – she wasn't to be seen – laughter and shouts came from the bathroom – the visual shock and the disbelief from Dad was apparent. He said "God, maybe it's right, maybe she should be here."

"Believe me Dad, this is where she belongs."

Veronica walked out of the bathroom, hair in a towel, dressed in her silk gown, smelling and looking gorgeous.

"Now then chuck"

"Hiya Dad!"

They hugged and cried. Half an hour later, he was sat in front of the TV, only to respond to "Hey Dad, are you deaf?"

I had decided to stay that night – I felt so protective and wanted to control things.

It was apparent that the house was slowly filling up with her friends. I sat by Veronica's side, reluctant to move, just happy to be by her – I felt her comfort, her strength – she laughed, she joked, she cried. I drank, they smoked and all was OK. Some of Veronica's oldest and closest friends arrived from London – her old boyfriend wanted to know the details – I was standing in the kitchen with him – I explained – he collapsed. He was out for almost 20 seconds. He really loved Veronica and Veronica loved him. My friend phoned, I'm sure I was affected by the passive smoke of cannabis and the drink – yet the perception of the scene being beautiful was, and still is, very real.

I started dropping hints for people to leave – as some left – more arrived. It was 10.30pm. Eventually they left.

I was anxious about where her boyfriend should sleep. I didn't want her to be disturbed – God – who am I to dictate to them where they sleep? Vron soon put me right, they slept together, only right, making the most of the nights they had left. I slept in the corridor on the floor nodding on and off. I remember listening to her breathing, very deep and regular, I was waiting until I was sure her boyfriend was asleep. I would then go in and sit by her.

Thursday, Day 5
I woke her up at 6am – making sure she had her tablets, ensuring she was free from pain, but also hoping we would have time together on our own to talk. We talked about her will, all the things she had missed off, she talked about dad and how much she loved him and how much he cared. She explained about what her funeral should be like and who she wanted to be with her at the end. She showed me how to anoint her candles and indicated the one she wanted lighting when she would start lapsing into a coma, when the candle burnt down – she said she would not be Vron as we know her – how right she was.

Later on that morning she had a bath, an abscess on her graft arm burst – I had warned everyone what to do because of the risk of Hepatitis – we had plenty of supplies and once her arm was dressed she looked and felt much better.

Throughout the day, friends and relatives would visit. It was difficult for anyone to say goodbye. Vron invited them all back, some said "see ya!" when they really meant goodbye – those that said goodbye meant it, wept and hugged, and Vron gave them precious words to take away with them.

She smoked a lot that day and was quite sick – vomiting several times. I told her off – she laughed!

Aunty Clare arrived – she came, immediately we felt her presence – she was calm and so full of love. Her conviction for religion was not obvious but her spirituality was. We felt she was a representative of our mother – you see – she was my mums best friend – it seemed that we were all determined to make up for the dissatisfying death of our mother. Later that night the family outnumbered the friends for the first time. There was a moment when Aunty Clare moved towards Vron – took her hands and spoke – what I learned later to be the 'talking in tongues' – no one knew what she was saying – it seemed to be meaningless garble. Veronica's reaction to this at the time seemed like total relaxation and pleasure. After half an hour of this talk Veronica said she had never experienced such beautiful words. She said it gave her strength, calm, warmth and rest.

It was obvious that evening she was tired.

I too slept quite well.

Friday, Day 6
She was tired – deterioration became apparent. Vron thought she might die today. A friend of hers had predicted that she would meet her mum on a Friday. She had already gone beyond what the medics had said, and I could not see any gross confusion or deterioration, however, I increased her medication as she was becoming a little anxious about pressure symptoms around her abdomen and knees. Aunty Clare sat with her most of the day, reading parts of the Bible, the priest visited and she received the Last Rites.

Later that afternoon, Veronica fell asleep. Time passed, it got beyond the time Veronica's tablets were due. I went over and tried to wake her quietly, the family were all there. I was conscious of them watching my actions, they all looked to me for explanation and expectations. I told them I would let them know when Veronica was in a coma. I pinched her ear lobes, moved her chin, felt her pulse, looked at her eyes – for nearly fifteen minutes I tried to gently wake her without success.

I began to feel she would not wake. I wiped her face, crying and talking to her. My sisters and father came forward, all crying – they too had thought as I had, that this was it – just as her friend came in and said goodbye – Veronica opened her eyes and said "What's up? I'm hungry, any black pudding?"

An hour later, she was eating bacon, black pudding, eggs and mushrooms. It was to be her last good meal.

I went home that night knowing the decline had started and also realising, not wanting to leave her again.

Saturday, Day 7
This was a quiet day, only her closest friends were around, she slept for long periods and her medication was increased. The day seemed to go very quickly, coping with her nausea, irritability and her lack of co-ordination.

Despite this, she still enjoyed and insisted upon, as she did every day, to have her bath, hair and nails done. It was to be her last day in the bath. She seemed to liven up towards the evening. She had spent some time alone during the day with Dad. She said she was at peace with him. That night, we were only family together – all sat round her, we were all physically somehow touching, close.

Veronica took a deep breath, looked around and said "I love you all, it's great to have a family like you." and I cried.

Sunday, Day 8
She was too weak to have a bath, my sisters gave her a bed bath, she enjoyed the fun, she slept a lot, ate nothing – just her ice cubes. She did a final check on all the books she had written in. Today, she said her goodbye to my children. How do you explain to six year olds? Veronica did – a child's heaven apparently in where rainbows start and finish, where care

bears live and smurfs play, where angels sing and where a lot of lovely people live – who are all there to love and hug you. The kids went away happy – the pain was obvious in Veronica's face.

Later that night, friends came again, invited by Vron's boyfriend and difficult for Vron to turn away. One of the friends was a drag artist. The scene later that night was Veronica and five of her friends sitting on her bed – and others on the couch – watching this man dressed in women's clothing and Christmas tree lights – dancing. Veronica laughed.

Monday, Day 9
Veronica left her bed twice – once to have a pee (she didn't and has not passed urine for 12 months) the other – to go to the bathroom to check if her hair was OK. Her deterioration was now serious, her co-ordination was bad, her lucid moments were short and few. That night she told me she was going to die. I asked if she was ready, she said yes.

Later that night, she lit her final candle, it was her last night with her boyfriend.

Tuesday, Day 10
My anxieties revolved around ensuring her tablets were taken and kept down and wondering when to start giving her the pain killing suppositories. Her spasms were getting worse – I increased her medication, which seemed to work.

She slept most of the day, however, there were times when she attempted to get up – she wanted to sit up, then after a few seconds she would fall backwards very uneasily – was she distressed?

Every aspect of care was considered – we had charts for mouth care, general care, positioning and medication. I was so tired. A friend of mine rang me – saying "you've done your bit, let others do some". It sounded like common sense, I went home. I slept a good five hours – Veronica had a restless night.

Wednesday, Day 11

As I walked in that morning, I saw my exhausted sisters and Veronica on the bed – she had not had sufficient sedation – I immediately gave her more. Realising the suppositories were going to be inadequate, I contacted our doctor and demanded intramuscular medication – I also rang the hospital – they suggested diamorphine – the thing Veronica didn't want, a matter of principle, however, as she knew, sometimes, her brother knows best.

After giving her the prescribed medication by injection, she began to be more restful. Her pulse started to change. After midnight, she turned cold and clammy, her heart was weak. I knew she would die soon. I held her hand. I saw her frail body beginning to let go. She moved onto her back – she was gasping yet not distressed, only reflexes were keeping her going. At 02.25, I woke my sister and dad, at 02.27 we all held her in our arms. At 02.28, she stopped breathing.

I sat for half an hour just fiddling with her hair and then I knew, things had to be done. She had left instructions for my sisters regarding final preparation.

I went into the kitchen with Dad and we talked about running, boats and navigation.

I then sat in the corner of the room where Veronica laid, looking so beautiful and peaceful and I cried through closed eyes for 4 hours. The doctor arrived with the certificate; he said some words about respect for Veronica. My sisters did the phoning.

The undertakers came, she was smiling. It was as if she was laughing at them wearing yellow Marigold plastic gloves, instead of the traditional white gloves (they were told to protect themselves from Hepatitis!). It was hard and painful to say goodbye again, finally, as she lay in her coffin.

The funeral was a fitting end, her grave was cramped with flowers. My single carnation stood out alone. The message read

"Thanks Ronks, for the love, strength and words.

Sleep peacefully. Love from your Big Brother.

x x x x x x x x "

This experience had a profound effect on us as a family. We shared our love and supported each other in such a way that we transformed what could seem to be by some an extremely stressful and distressing event into a celebration whereby Veronica's initial courage to face her own death became a model of strength, which enabled us to let her go with pride and dignity.

During those days Veronica dealt with all her unfinished business, said all she wanted to say, saw who she wanted to see and died peacefully.

Veronica had quite an opportunity to and indeed contemplated taking her own life, but she faced up to her situation and fought the best way she could. When the odds were finally too much, she stopped fighting and found a different type of courage; a courage which enabled her to finally discover her true meaning, her self, and her acceptance of herself.

I wrote this account shortly after her death as I sensed the need to recall the experience as a way of working through my grief. It's relevant now as this diary is also about finding courage to discover my own true meaning and acceptance – before it's too late as it was for my sister Veronica.

Veronica was also a prolific writer of diaries. In these she would write her own poetry which could give a sad insight into my sister's lost and lonely soul.

Where is this? Who am I?
Afraid of life, a fool to cry.
A sure way out, an urge to die,
a dream to live before goodbye.

Always I must question why?
Is it all an endless lie?
I must rebel, I must defy,
Must fight the chains that hold me down
Put on a face, tears of a clown,
To not be afraid of being myself
Strange, crazy, mixed up kid.

O God, still this fiery pain inside
Give me peace
Controlled desire waiting to unleash
Love sweet and rich like honey wine
To pour over your wounds and quench your thirst
I love you now and even though our
love must be cursed
You belong in my heart
I belong in your arms
I'll protect you inside from all
the lies, kiss your feet
your side, your palms, wipe the sweat
from your eyes
Don't cry
I have nothing now without you
but you're in my heart to stray
You'll come back don't leave
it too long to realise, I pray.

If ever I should find a place
Where I can see your gentle face
Although we are not one as yet
The time will come "have we met?"
I look for you, you wait for me
Only the angels watch to see
And guide our paths together soon
You are my sun, I am your moon
Together we will face the world

Where oh where does my destiny lay?
Why do I care, what's wrong with today?
Why must I lay alone in my room?
Why do I long to be back in the womb?
Why do I choose the world for my card?
Why can't you see beyond this façade?
Why do I always have to ask why?
Why should you care?
Leave me to cry.

I also remember Veronica's laughter, her wicked sense of humour; she was very bright, intelligent and had a great sense of intuition. She felt passionately about things and we were good play mates. I remember taking her fishing. I remember her reciting poetry and singing. She was beautiful, a model and today still visits me, her presence I feel from time to time in quiet moments. It is time, after 21 years, to let her go.

Goodbye, my dear, dear little sister.

Finally – the finally is from Veronica's diary – a sad story of how she saw her life.

What do you think of little girl, when you look at me?
What do those innocent eyes behold, little child of three.
You are at peace with mother earth where all is fresh and light,
you play in a world of fantasy made for your delight.
Hello little girl with clear blue eyes,
I see you're still free from deceit and lies.
How do you see the world now that you are five
You love the birds and butterflies
You love your little kitten,
and the playful puppy down the road – you've never been bitten
Little girl you age so fast,
the tears begin to come
Why do I have to do as I'm told?
Why can't I just have fun?
Why do I have to go to school?
Why are the boys so horrible and cruel?
Why does my daddy never come home?
Please tell me what I have done.
Confusion fills your little soul,
Now that you are seven
Why do people have to go and
where is this place called heaven?
So you've started to run away little girl,
The smiles' gone from your face
You don't want them to see your tears
Because no one wants to hear your fears
and you hate this horrible place.

You feel the need to be alone
and so you build a den
You see and feel a lot of truth
for a little girl of ten.
You can't understand why people die
or why you alone often cry
or why you're the only one to see them fight
if they love each other why must they hurt
and why can't I never seem to do things right?
And what's all this stuff about birds and bees?
Don't tell me life gets worse
My heart's so full of questions,
you're frightened one day it will burst
Now you have to make your stand
The lines begin to deepen on your hand
Fourteen I know is a difficult time
So join the rebels band.
If no-one's going to tell me why,
I'm going to do as I like
I like my friends, they're full of fun
I don't care if they're not right.
What business is it of yours what I do?
You've never cared before.
You don't want me to have any fun
o mother you're such a bore
You're on your own now little girl
for you refuse to listen to me
You don't give a damn for wrong and right
you've got a shield and you will fight
You must fight a lot in the years to come
before you see the light
So all I can do is watch and wait
Now you're filled with venom and hate
til you come back to where you belong
You have to learn to cope with things
Although it seems unfair
and now I see the devil has come
to tempt you to his lair.

My thoughts:

Each child is unique and have their own special thoughts, and no doubt – each child, from time to time, will feel alone – but no child should be left alone – we must strive to listen, understand, support and love our children growing and learning, so they can choose to turn to the light and away from the dark – never to be left in his lair.

THOUGHT FOR THE DAY
Find the courage, before it's too late.

01.02.2006   Day 132

A year before Veronica's death, a beautiful thing happened. My step daughter was born. I have grown to love her as my own daughter and I hope one day she learns to love me as her father. She is an amazing young woman and will make a difference in this World. Watch this space!!

Today, we visit the main attraction – the Alhambra Palace.

By the way – Fatmea has been very stubborn these last few days – still not beaten the emotion = vulnerable = eat and drink more connections. Still a battle. Must be stronger. Must be gentler on myself. Give myself a rest. I am tired inside.

THOUGHT FOR THE DAY
The world is in balance – how can I ?

02.02.2006   Day 133

Two million visitors a year walk this majestic experience standing proud in the foothills of the snow capped Sierra Nevada mountains. Starting our tour at 8.30am was a good idea as we avoided most of the group tours and cackling children. We were often on our own, soaking in the splendour of creation in honour of Kings and religion.

Over a thousand years old and built on endlessly, the Sultan's palace built synchronistically to the Islamic faith, the circle of splendour to Charles II and the water gardens with its flow of life around every corner and multiple levels. All this guarded by a fortress which can not surely have ever been breached.

We saw the sun rise and the snow glow pink and the white streets below shine brilliantly. It is here we explored not knowing where we were going, but somehow intuitively knew something at the end of it was special.

Sure enough, we found the church on the hill and a restaurant who's balcony overlooked the valley of Granada, opposite the Alhambra Palace. We soaked in the experience and toasted life and our daughter's birthday. Moving on in search of Cathedral wisdom, we entered glory and awe as we paid homage to the saints in the many beautiful chapels and altars. What a day!

It's good to soak it in, not think too hard, just be and enjoy.

THOUGHT FOR THE DAY
This is an incredible world!

03.02.2006   Day 134

The contrast in 'people shape' between Florida and Portugal/Spain is extreme. It seems that almost every other person in Florida is grossly obese. (I don't mean this derogatively – just extremely obese), whereas I have yet to see one in that same category here in the Mediterranean. Diet here is dominated by fish, I see few fast food outlets and certainly no all-u-can eat buffets.

Portions here seem smaller, eg: the tapas bar – where a 'selection of small tasters' seems part of the culture. It will be interesting to see how my two sisters are adapting to their new lives.

What choices will I make today I wonder?
Choices of behaviour
Choices of feelings
Choices of attention
Choices of reaction
Choices of connections
Choices of being
Choose now.

04.02.2006   Day 135

1000 souls lost in the Red Sea, went down with the sinking of an Egyptian Ferry. The design of which was similar to the Spirit of Free Enterprise ferry which capsized in the North Sea off Zeebrugger years ago. This same type of ferry was sold on to the Egyptians. Is there any moral or ethical obligation in this transaction? Should an owner of a dog that has been abused sell this on to a new owner with a young family, knowing that it has a history of unprovoked attacks? God rest their souls and hope that one day their families find peace.

It was good to catch up with both my sisters yesterday. Christine and Andy renovating an old farm cottage among the trees of olive, citrus, orange, lemon, cherry, almond, apple and fig. On a hillside, looking over a valley, surrounded by mountains. They now have a kitchen, toilet, new roof and have great plans to build this palace in the idyllic countryside.

Barbara is now well established amongst the orange groves, pottering in her beautiful garden and walking her dogs and the neighbours dogs to the beach every day – a beach she calls her own. She has made some good friends.

THOUGHT FOR THE DAY
In search of peace and happiness?

05.02.2006   Day 136

European embassies on fire, violent protests and deaths in the streets, death threats and war declaration to those who insult the Islamic faith. A Danish newspaper published cartoon images of the prophet Mohammed. This is prohibited in the Muslim faith, and the newspaper I believe showed an ignorance and insensitivity to the Muslim religion. I believe in the freedom of the press, but not without moral and social obligation to understand the impact of what it prints.

However, the degree of anger released shows how tense and fragile the relationship is between Christians and Muslims and probably Jewish religions. Forgiveness and the love of our fellow human are a basis of all these religions – now is the time for restraint and understanding.

Worshipping false gods, inappropriate images are also common to us all – let's use this occasion to recognise what we share – not what divides us.

THOUGHT FOR THE DAY
God is greater than any image man can make, God is greater than any emotion these images provoke, forgiveness and understanding is close to an expression of God.

06.02.2006   Day 137

It was good to see my sisters making new lives for themselves – it was tough to say goodbye.

THOUGHT FOR THE DAY
Home is where the heart is – where is the heart?

07.02.2006   Day 138

This diary is turning into a record of 'my life into six months'. I will finish this record soon. Probably before my target weight of 14 stone, but well on the way and confident of achieving it and most importantly, keeping it.

For some, losing a lot of weight will be about transforming their lives. It may involve reappraising who you are and what you want. It is likely to mean taking an honest look at your self, inside and out, and choosing what your life priorities are.

For me, well, I have felt I have been doing the above for most of my adult life to varying degrees of success! This tells me it is a life long journey. The destination being that moment or point, when you know you have arrived, that point of just being you in harmony with everything and everyone else. I also believe that point of arrival can be transient and temporary – in life events will move you off back onto the journey.

For me, I recognise I will always be on my journey of self discovery – I change, the World changes, the people around me change, therefore my choices will depend on my awareness of what's going on in this ever changing dynamic.

This diary is about my choice to live a fitter and healthier life. It recognises my vulnerability to over eating and over drinking, it shouts honesty about my potential for addiction to food and alcohol all of which are masks, defences, protection to avoid my right to be happy just as I am.

THOUGHT FOR THE DAY
Sometimes it's worth pausing a moment on your journey and checking out where you actually are.

08.02.2006   Day 139

Back to my nursing days. A story about trust. Peter was a young man of about 26. He had lived with his parents up until a few months prior to being admitted to the acute male psychiatric ward. He had to be restrained by police, after attacking his father and making threats to his neighbours. Peter was diagnosed as having paranoid schizophrenia where everyone and everything in the world was perceived with suspicion. His initial days on the ward were routinely monitored. Dressed in an institutional dressing gown and heavily sedated, Peter's world must have seemed like a confused dream state. He would keep his own company, not talk to anyone and move away from anyone who approached him.

I took it upon myself to spend some time, just sitting with him initially, bringing him a mug of tea, passing him a newspaper, then when he was allowed to get dressed – walk in the hospital grounds with him. He was compulsorily detained, which means legally he was not allowed to leave the grounds as he was considered to be a danger to himself and others. One morning as I arrived on duty, I was asked to accompany my colleague to Peter's home address.

He had absconded yesterday and his parents rang the hospital to say he was at home but quite distressed.

Peter's home was an old farm cottage on the outskirts of a small town, about 30 miles from the hospital. We arrived to be greeted by two very anxious elderly parents. Peter had locked himself in his bedroom and was expressing anger and threats to neighbours across the street, whom he thought were directing obscene gestures toward him.

The worrying thing was, Peter's father thought he might have a hunting gun with him. We decided to call the local doctor and the police but informed them both to approach discreetly. I thought since I was the one who knew Peter better than most, it may be worth persuading him to come out of his room and come back with us of his own accord.

I walked up the old narrow staircase and knocked on his door.

"Peter, it's Mike – can you talk?"

Silence.

"Peter, it's Mike – remember – from the Hospital?"

"I know who you are – piss off!"

"Your mum and dad are concerned – they want you to come down"

"Fuck off."

"We are worried about you. You will get better but you must let us look after you"

With that – the door opened.

Peter stood face to face with myself – he was a big chap, about my age, his face was red, his eyes watering and I noticed his knuckles white with rage wrapped around this shotgun he held across his chest.

My stomach churned, I felt sick and I felt my knees shake.

"Peter" I said with a quivering voice –

"Let me pass" he said

"Come down, let's have a cup of tea – I'm sure we can sort things out..."

I couldn't believe I was doing this – face to face with a paranoid escaped patient with a shotgun in his hands.

He turned, he went back in his room. I sat on the stairs shaking.

At that moment, the police had arrived, followed shortly by the doctor. Reinforcements – I thought I would try once more.

"Peter, come down now with me, let's chat about it, have a cup of tea and maybe something to eat."

"I'm not going back to that loony bin!"

"If you don't come down soon and start discussing it, then you will have to be taken back."

"OK, but promise me I won't go back tonight."

"I'll see what I can do, but leave the gun in your room."

Meanwhile, my colleague had briefed the police and the doctor as to the recent events. The police had informed an armed response unit. I was now at the bottom of the stairs, Peter came down gingerly, without the gun. As he entered the room, a police siren deafened the quiet country village, Peter made a run for the front door, the police jumped, restrained and handcuffed him. The doctor gave him an intramuscular injection in his backside.

As he lay with his face down, I'll never forget the next moment – he turned his head, stared right at me and said "I trusted you, you bastard!"

Our relationship never recovered from that incident, even as he improved, he would avoid me and I know one shouldn't take your work personally, but this one hurt for a long time.

THOUGHT FOR THE DAY
What does it take to trust some one, can it ever be regained once broken?

09.02.2006　Day 140

So, the weight is stable at the moment. Nearly 2 weeks in Portugal / Spain made it difficult to say no to the local produce! However, I am very confident now it will drop off. I realise that starving oneself does not work – all this does is slow the metabolism down and make the fat cells even more desperate for food. – so when you do eat – you're likely to store excess even more. One of the secrets I believe is to eat little and often – not starve all day than binge eat in the evening – which is a regular pattern of mine.

Going to bed slightly peckish or hungry may be a good thing. Also, continue on drinking plenty of water and having regular exercise. We are on a winner – Fatmea is getting less dominant!

THOUGHT FOR THE DAY
Those that have less often have more.

10.02.2006   Day 141

Part of my work has involved helping an airline prepare their airport staff to respond appropriately in the event of a major incident, eg: major delays, bad landing or the unthinkable – an air crash. A particularly emotional and intense workshop I was running was in Los Angeles where half way through the morning session, a member of staff broke down.

Through her team she told the story of a recent accident a few days ago where a young engineer had been killed on the runway.

Somehow, as the Jumbo 747 was being pushed back, he approached the front wheel – something to do with a pin that had to be secured or released at the right time. His foot got caught and he was crushed to death – dying almost immediately. Unfortunately – this was witnessed by many as the Gate was clearly visible by waiting passengers and staff. This participant in the workshop was one of the witnesses. The workshop I ran stresses the importance of listening to, and experiencing an understanding of, feelings – this was enough to trigger off what was a well needed cathartic release of stress and trauma. She had attempted to put it to the back of her mind, be strong and carry on – this is not the best way of dealing with traumatic events. Following the workshop, she was able to get the appropriate support.

Understanding the effect a traumatic event has on you is important. Talking about it to someone supportive and understanding helps. Finding its meaning and purpose is more difficult – but many do channel their grief or experience into positive endeavours helping others in the process.

11.02.2006   Day 142

Our attorney in Florida advises us to give the mortgage company
time to verify that fraud has actually taken place. If they do – then
they will not fight us or make a claim on the mortgage we didn't take
out on our Florida home. It is going to take a little longer but should
cost us less in legal fees. Everyone else has gone quiet. We think
these fraudsters are going to get away with it. Perhaps we should
alert the media and get a warning out to Villa owners. We may do
this – but it's probably wise to get our house back first.

THOUGHT FOR THE DAY
Patience is a virtue – but why does it have to take so long?

12.02.2006   Day 143

Spending time with family often involves reminiscing and sharing
images of each other in the past. We have learned to keep this
positive as it is too easy to tap into each others' grief. My big sister
recalls the times she used to look out for me. I remember the time
I fell out of a tree to get a ball for my younger sister – hurt my arm
– no one believed it was serious – until my uncle took me on a sledge
in the snow – I fell off and came back screaming. I was about 9 years
old and it wasn't until my big sister shouted "get him to a hospital"
that eventually, a serious break in the arm was diagnosed. First time
my picture was in the paper was as my arm was plastered in the
casualty department where they were doing an article in the local
press.

Even younger, during our holidays at Barmston, Filey, in the
bungalow on the cliff edge that eventually eroded away. I stepped
on a 'weevil' fish. I remember the pain today. Again, big sister was
there shouting at my father to take me to hospital – I remember the

journey – my foot was in my mouth – trying to stop the pain.

Another hospital incident involved, again, days of pain 'stomach ache or too many sweets and apples' as I recall I was accused of. But then, big sister insisted on the doctor being called and emergency admission to hospital for appendicitis and operation to remove it occurred. I was about 10 I think.

These are distant images and perceptions of the roles we played as children. Why did I have to make so much fuss to be taken seriously as a Child? Was it something to do with being the only boy? Where were my mum and dad in all this? Too busy in the shop?

The first 11 years of my life, I remember as a long playful summer. I loved school, I loved our street, I loved my friends. I loved the freedom and the security of knowing that someone would always be home. I loved playing with my younger sisters. Each Sunday morning, we would spend hours turning the furniture upside down and using the cushions to build our homes and dens – all this before mum and dad woke up – great memories.

THOUGHT FOR THE DAY
The freedom to play and to be hugged by a loving parent at least at the end of the day should be the divine right of every child.

13.02.2006   Day 144

Note e-mail to my friend this morning.

"Have you ever thought what your core purpose in life was?

A purpose or way of being that you are particularly good at?

Better than most because of your uniqueness. It appears to me that it may have something to do with connectedness. This may have been with you longer than you think. In BT, weren't you initially connecting wires and cables to enable information and people to be connected? This eventually developed into connecting people. You now continue to connect, people to people, ideas to people in situations, right at the moment – making a difference to people's lives.

Why did I offer this thought? I'm not sure – I got a few Kung Hei Fat Choi's last week, wondered how you were, woke up this morning reflecting on connectedness and you came to mind. So, chose to follow it up. Luv Mike."

14.02.2006 Valentine's Day   Day 145

Today we have an opportunity to express our love to our partners. I believe expressing love every day is important but today is a good moment for giving it some special attention. My valentine card to my wife reads:

"I must be the luckiest man on earth! I don't fully understand why our destinies collided, but I am still excited and long for your company, even when we are apart for a few hours.

You are so integral to my life and I love you more than you can bare.

Our partnership is so complimentary and based on total trust, acceptance and care for one another. You put up with my occasional melancholic grumpiness, I put up with your frequent continental temperament! Put up with is not quite right because it's you and I love every bit of you.

You have enriched my life to more than I ever thought could be possible and you continue to surprise me with your spontaneity, fun, vulnerability and strength.

If I could receive half the love you are capable of giving then I would be even more fulfilled. Thank you for being my wife, our journey together, now and forever will be wondrous, beautiful, exciting, mysterious, full of learning and laughter, all because, whatever we do – wherever we are our hearts are beating as one.

You have my love always every micro second of every universal moment.

Hugs and kisses, your husband."

15.02.2006   Day 146

Fatmea under control! No snacks, drink in moderation, mainly at weekends, cut down on bread, pasta, potatoes. Increase fruit and veg. Less meat, more fish. Cereal for breakfast, fruit, soup and / or salad for lunch, meat or fish and veg for dinner. Exercise 30 minutes aerobic exercise on the cross trainer at least 5 times a week. It's a simple formulae – it's what I want – it's not hard.

All this, combined with a greater sense of connectedness.

Connection between my mind, body and spirit. How these connect also with the world I live in. An increased awareness of who I am and how I relate. An understanding of the impact I make and the choices I have.

A sense of delight and wonderment each day knowing I will be surprised by a connection, a miracle, a visit, an expression of love, something new, each one a celebration.

Physically, changing shape, mentally getting stronger, spiritually on the journey.

Spring is around the corner, buds and green shoots are just beginning to show.

New growth, new beginnings!

THOUGHT FOR THE DAY
To be 'present' is a 'gift' to ourselves and for others.

16.02.2006   Day 147

This is my favourite prayer – the prayer of St Francis of Assisi.

Lord, make me an instrument of your peace,
Where there is hatred, let me sow love;
where there is injury, pardon;
where there is doubt, faith;
where there is despair, hope;
where there is darkness, light;
where there is sadness, joy;

O Divine Master, grant that I may not so much seek to be consoled as to console;
to be understood as to understand;
to be loved as to love.

For it is in giving that we receive;
it is in pardoning that we are pardoned;
and it is in dying that we are born to eternal life.

THOUGHT FOR THE DAY
What miracle will we witness today, inspirational moments are all around us – can we experience them?

17.02.2006   Day 148

Our government has just voted to ban smoking in all public areas! At last, common sense prevails!!

So what if £9 billion a year might be lost in taxes if a lot more people gave up – think of the savings related to a healthier nation.

My grandfather was a smoker – he died of lung disease, my uncle was a smoker – he died of throat cancer, my mother in law was a smoker – she died of lung cancer. My boys smoke and it hurts me deeply to see them choosing to breath in those cancerous fumes.

There is nothing worse than breathing in someone else's smoke – especially when you are eating – so well done our government!

I smoked on and off between the ages of 17 and 25. It took real positive will power to say no more – that's it! Choose healthy lungs and not cancerous – and oh by the way – what money you save!!

So, you can give up smoking – if you really want to. You can lose weight if you really want to. You can achieve anything if you believe in yourself and believe it is possible. I like this quote – which I think is from Ghandi: 'The limits in this world are mainly based on limits created by our perceived barriers and fears.'

There's also a sense in me about freedom to choose what I want to do for the rest of my life – no barriers, no fear.

I have mentioned previously in this diary the importance of making the most of the time left. It's official – average life expectancy

190

for me in the UK is now 78.8 years – which means I have (although I hope to live a little longer say – 80+) 27.2 years left. If I manage to keep the weight off and keep fit, then we can hope for at least 20 years of active all round fitness.

I can do a lot in 20 years – but what? I also like the quote which I am not sure where it is from – perhaps 'one world' an anthem sang at the Rugby Union World Cup – it's something like 'Take your place in history, live your life with dignity'.

So, transforming fear, serving others, live with dignity – if I can achieve this then it almost feels like it doesn't matter what I do – or I mean – I will find meaning in all my work and work and opportunity will find me.

THOUGHT FOR THE DAY
Do yourself a favour – believe you can succeed!

18.02.2006   Day 149

It's feared that up to 1800 people have died in a massive mudslide in the Philippines. A remote village was swamped and a school full of children disappeared. The rainy season had just started – 2 weeks downpour. Officials say they were warned – it takes a lot to abandon your home for something that might not happen. They paid with their lives – God rest their souls.

I have a tenuous connection to the Philippines in that my father worked out there in the early 1980's. He befriended a girl called Mary from the village of Mia-Mia on the island of Mindora. He had a boat moored at the Manila Yacht Club and I suspect would rather be there than here in the cold UK with demands upon him from an attention seeking family. I do remember him saying that the villagers were extremely welcoming and had a wonderful life style although living on very little. It's difficult to imagine the pain and anguish these people are going through – lives devastated – community destroyed. How can we help?

In contrast, here I am sitting contemplating, sun shining, bright blue and white sky, birds singing – wondering what today will bring and what I will bring the day.

THOUGHT FOR THE DAY
Solid home, solid lives, free spirit.

19.02.2006 Day 150

What does the future hold?
What do I want?
How would I like to be?
Have I the courage to be bold?
To go back to the font
So I can be me
Who am I?
Who do I want to be?
Alone, together, we shall see
Let it be, or make it happen,
Live each day
See where you go
Be open, honest, listen and learn
The truth will lead to inner peace
Be calm, quiet inside and let others
Love you
Be patient with others anger, be gentle
With them and yourself
Be happy and enjoy the simple things
Let it be

THOUGHT FOR THE DAY
Simply this, this moment is now, and is special.

20.02.2006 Day 151

This weekend was a family weekend. Mainly my wife's side getting together with her brother from Houston, Texas – he's lived there for years and he values his roots so visits us at least once a year.

So, family party, meal out and on Sunday – time with my Grandson. Families – with so much love and history involved there is rarely an occasion when tension or problems of some sort with at least one member occurs. It's also difficult to judge how much one gets involved. Even offering help, showing concern, making helpful suggestions can be seen as interfering and be resented. Perhaps just saying we are here if you need us, thinking of you, is enough.

THOUGHT FOR THE DAY
Why do some people find it so difficult to ask for help?

21.02.2006   Day 152

If you started reading this diary because you had a question about losing weight – the chances are you have already. How much you have lost is not important – however, your approach to looking after yourself, your insights about who you are and how you relate to others is.

The will to lose weight has to be real choice. It is relatively easy to lose a stone, or even 20lbs by going on a strict crash or fad diet. This will not work – weight will go back on within months.

Weight needs to be lost gradually – it's taken me 50 years to get to where I am now – why should it only take a few months to lose the excess? I have lost 2 stone so far (28lbs). I want to lose another stone.

I will do this – slowly and in parallel to my development. My development being focussed on increasing my awareness, my ability to be me, my ability and sensitivity to be with others in such a way that helps. This doesn't mean being the 'do gooder' – it means just 'being' and follow up on coincidences and intuition.

So losing weight is a bigger question than being physically fit – it's about being mentally and spiritually fit too.

It may be that you are reading this diary not because you have an issue about your weight, but because you're curious. Within your curiosity will be a question for yourself. It may be of value to you to identify – what *your* question is?

Being overweight is just one way of being unfit, others include too much alcohol, smoking, other drug addictions, other addictions, ie: gambling, too much stress, too much conflict, hate, anger – all contributing to masking, defending, wrestling against the core issue of who you really are.

Take your time, love others and yourself a little more.

Be still and quiet, ask yourself what's really important?

Get to know who you are, down to the core. Forgive yourself and others, celebrate what you have.

THOUGHT FOR THE DAY
Better to take your time when climbing up a mountain
– you can pause, soak in the views and enjoy the pounding
of your heart and the expansion of your lungs, the sense of
achievement and the ever changing horizon.

22.02.2006   Day 153

The swans glide majestically in the early morning mist along this royal waterway, which shouts of historical and momentous occasions. I am staying in what was the home of Sir Christopher Wren (the Architect of St Paul's Cathedral) now a hotel next to Windsor Castle – the seat of British Royalty. I am here when the swans are under threat of Bird Flu (now in France and the British Government nervous and unsure how to respond / prepare) and Prince Charles in court suing a newspaper for publishing extracts of his personal diary. Should he have the rights to privacy as any citizen should or are his written thoughts for the public domain? His thoughts and comments about the handover of Hong Kong to China were interesting; however, are we better off for knowing? What's the value? I am sure his diary will be a damn sight more interesting than mine – why is he writing – may be it's about choosing to publish at a time of his choice – or he just wants it to be a legacy for history.

For that matter – what will happen to this diary? At least it becomes a legacy which I am sure my family would be interested in once I have died – perhaps they read it before I die – perhaps others should read it. Will they gain from it? Will it help others? I will listen out for a sign that tells me what to do and to listen to my heart as to what the right thing is to do with these ramblings. I wish I had the time to wander round this Royal Windsor Castle – but alas, to work, my audience of eager managers aspiring to be better managers wait.

THOUGHT FOR THE DAY
Publish and be damned, make waves or wait for the tide to come in?

23.02.2006   Day 154

THOUGHT FOR THE DAY
Judge less, listen more, ask yourself why this moment, choose to be and become who you really are.

24.02.2006   Day 155

I pray that the Sunni and Shiite Muslim leaders work together for peace and condemn the extremist activity that attempts to divide them.

I pray that the Muslim world can forgive the minority of British and American soldiers for abusing their prisoners.

I pray that our soldiers in Iraq and Afghanistan stay safe – that the community recognise they are there to help the majority be safe and to live in peace.

I pray that large roofed buildings are built to withstand snow as more deaths have occurred, this time in Russia due to a market roof collapsing.

I pray that we can stop polluting the planet and somehow slow down or stop global warming so that lives and future generations can live with less weather extremes, disasters and flooding.

I pray that the violence inbred in some of our youths today is transformed and incidents like mobile phone videoing violent attacks stops.

I pray that those in long term care get better nutrition as it seems at the moment, they don't.

I pray that we are prepared for the nightmare situation where bird flu mutates and a pandemic of human flu devastates lives.

I pray that all abuse of human rights stop.

I pray we don't forget the continual struggle of those trying to put their lives back together after Tsunami, earth quakes, floods, hurricanes, bombs, mudslides, famine, disease and persecution.

I pray that all my family find success in happiness and health.

And, I pray that I continue to respect my body, listen to how I relate to this world and act out of love and integrity.

THOUGHT FOR THE DAY
I hope and pray that when my Grandson or Granddaughter reads this – the world is a better place.

25.02.2006   Day 156

Our bodies are amazing! It never stops, 24/7, not a second does it shut down or take a break. Even in sleep, our heart, lungs, brain, digestive system continue to work their miracle of renewal. Each cell in our body continually working, dieing and reborn again. We change continually. It makes sense therefore that from time to time, we give it a rest – yes? Hence, the importance of quiet time, relaxation with reflection – some call it prayer, some call it meditation, some call it a walk in the countryside. I am also wondering that it maybe worthwhile giving my digestive system a rest occasionally. Not to stop eating as this makes things worse, but to have an occasional light day with dominance of liquids or soft foods and no meat. I don't know if there is any scientific research to indicate whether this is beneficial but it seems to me common sense to go easy on yourself sometimes and give your 'guts' a holiday.

THOUGHT FOR THE DAY
Rest a while with me.

26.02.2006   Day 157

When the sun shines, how do you feel?
When the rain falls, who do you recall?
When the wind blows, what do you think?
When the snow settles, what memory stirs?
When the clouds gather before a storm,
What excites you and where is your fear?
When the stillness of dawn wakes, where are you?
When sunset burns, what is satisfying you?
When there is calm, who are you?

THOUGHT FOR THE DAY
One thing is certain, sunset and dawn.

27.02.2006   Day 158

Here I am at one of the most famous Children's Hospitals in the World. Over the last 5 years, I have helped them recover from disaster, built their top team, trained their best people, transformed and developed their culture and all in the cause of ensuring that children continue to get the best care in the world.

This is work I enjoy and feel good that somehow, the events I design and run, impact on the kids and their families. Now, I work with them only on occasion. This time, it's helping the top team take stock, where are they – what's the next few years looking like, are they up for it both in their understanding of the changes in the NHS and in terms of the way they work together?

My job? Somehow, my presence, my questioning, support and challenge needs to move them toward a state of confidence and a greater collective understanding as to the way forward.

I am never fully confident before these events, I always carry some self doubt, more so this time because I have let go of a large part of the input/presentation to the directors themselves. I am more confident with those elements I can control – so – must let go – take a risk, out of uncertainty comes learning and change – a bit like life really!

THOUGHT FOR THE DAY
How do I make the right choice, intuitively, at the right time?

28.02.2006   Day 159

Today, I visit an old previous place of work. The oldest mental institution in the World. A beautiful building built for £3,000 by the Trustees of York in 1775. I serve on a panel to hear cases of people who are legally detained against their will under the Mental Health Act. We read the reports from the nurse, psychiatrist and social worker, then all together with the patient, we discuss his or her future and whether they are safe to return to the community. It's quite a responsibility, because on one hand – it seems straightforward and usually very clear through the reports that the patient should continue to be detained – on the other – they have rights and it's up to us to challenge the professionals as much as judge how well the patient is. It feels strange going back to my work roots. I see familiar faces, past students who are now senior managers, even old patients still walking the corridors with familiar strides and sounds. I used to love my work. The daily uncertainty and unpredictability of mental illness and the challenge of coping with extremes of behaviour attracted me. In a way, it's a shame that when you like something, it often means you become good at it – which increases the chances of promotion, which eventually takes you away from what you liked doing in the first place. However, I think I have somehow managed to design a 'work routine' that still finds me coping with unpredictability and extremes of behaviour!

Fatmea by the way can now be grabbed hold of with two hands. She is seen as an unnecessary case of flab.

She is stubborn, but there is no doubt, the true me is winning. She is going, I am doing the right 'thin'!

Goodbye Fatmea, hello Thinmea!!

THOUGHT FOR THE DAY
Imagine yourself thin, act as if you are and you will be.

01.03.2006   Day 160

Amazingly, the people of New Orleans pull out all the stops to have the Mardis Gras – mixed feelings for those whose homes still lay in ruin yet a determination to celebrate a great city. A feast, a celebration before a period of giving and abstinence. Ash Wednesday today – Christians recognise 40 days before Easter as a period of atonement and 'giving something up for lent'. Yesterday was Shrove Tuesday where the 'striving to repent' meaning is probably lost in the tradition of tossing pancakes.

It's freezing with bright blue sky outside and the east coast (just a few miles away) and moors are under several inches of snow. Out troops are still getting killed in Iraq and they want to come home. Iraq is a mess, Shiite and Sunni attacking each other, American and British soldiers killed almost on a daily basis – I suspect the answer lay in the Religious leaders hands and prayer.

My niece should be giving birth today to a baby girl – Natasha – a miracle, as at one time my niece was told she was unlikely to have any children. This will be her second.

The police are confident in catching the armed robbers of the largest ever bank raid of £54 million last week; they terrorised a security manager's family to get access to the money. They will be caught.

The winter Olympics in Turin were a spectacle to watch over the last few weeks, even though the Brit's only got one silver medal. Well done Shelley!

A government report which has taken 18 months to complete has managed to state the bleeding obvious – our children are getting fatter! Despite the initiatives and investments in educating about healthy eating – they recognise there is a lack of coordination of all concerned parties – now where have we heard that one before?

THOUGHT FOR THE DAY
What a rich, diverse, surprising, predictable, wonderful world we live in – it's good to be alive!!

02.03.2006   Day 161

I have work in London these next few days. Travelling to and in London will never be the same. This was reinforced yesterday when the Mayor, Ken Livingstone (who is notorious for putting his strong opinion forward without too much consideration!), says "It's inevitable we are going to be attacked again!!" So, who will be killed? This is the success of terrorism – psychological warfare – they win. However, the situation can not stop us getting on with our lives – it's a risk we all have to take. None of us must stop living because of the fear and anxiety related to something that might or might not happen to us. We can acknowledge the fear, the worry – then place it somewhere else or transform it – for if it occupies too much space – it takes away what you have right now.

THOUGHT FOR THE DAY
You face this moment now, deal with what's real not with what might or might not happen.

03.03.2006   Day 162

If you are reading this diary in a logical way, ie: day after day in sequence, and you have got to today and you have a question about your health – then I assume you have done something about it.

If you are still over eating or over drinking, then I suspect you are in denial. This means it's too difficult for you to acknowledge you have a problem – and easier to continue as you are. 'Denial' is clever because you may have some slight adjustment to your behaviour, eg: eat a little less or have a few days off the booze, but the overall picture remains. If this is the case – it's time to revisit what's important and take control. When I am in a situation where the 'old' me (Fatmea in dominance) is waking up, I enlist the help of my 'guardian angel'. This sounds strange I know – but all this is is an aspect of myself standing back, looking at me and speaking to me with pure honesty and giving me the courage to do the 'right thin'.

THOUGHT FOR THE DAY
Listen to your angel, find the courage and choose to be free.

04.03.2006   Day 163

Brilliant white snow sparkling in the sun. Cold, crisp and clear. My mind is blank – perhaps this is a good thing?

THOUGHT FOR THE DAY
Can you think too much?

05.03.2006   Day 164

If you talk long enough with an apparent stranger you will find something that connects you. Last night at a dinner dance, Carol and I discovered we were both under the same specialist cancer care consultant. I'm not now of course – she is and has been for the last 20 years, ever since she had both breasts removed and went through chemotherapy for Hodgkins disease (cancer of the lymph glands) at the age of 17. Two years ago, she woke up totally paralysed and now, after further treatment, can walk with help. Carol was told twice in her life that the chances of her living through her illness was unlikely – she is still here and fighting.

Her attitude and spirit is one to be admired, she's feisty and outspoken, has a great sense of humour – we were laughing at the advantages of being disabled! She is going to hire herself out for those who want to get best seats at sporting events, ie the companion with the wheelchair!

If you ever catch yourself feeling sorry for yourself – look around – you will find many people in circumstances a lot worse than you and probably with more courage to make the most of what they have!

THOUGHT FOR THE DAY
If you are able to dance – do so and be happy!

06.03.2006   Day 165

A strong theme this year in the film award ceremonies culminating yesterday in the Oscars is serious films with serious messages. Fantasy and blockbusters, violence and sensationalism – nowhere to be seen.

Recent statistics from consumer research tells us in the UK we are buying less fast food, less ready meals, less salt and snacks and more fruit and veg. McDonalds have just closed 50 stores in the UK and moves are starting to ban snacks and fizzy drinks in schools.

Tessa Jowells, our culture secretary, is under pressure because of her husband's complex financial affairs and suspected involvement with Italian Political friendship involving less than straightforward money transactions.

The head of the Anglican Church, Dr Rowan Williams, is an unhappy man struggling to keep his flock together due to the difference in opinion over homosexuality.

My great niece 'Natasha' was born a few days ago, 8lb, 4oz. Mum and baby doing well.

My son, Matthew, is living on his own again, my other son Thomas, with his wife Claire and my grandson Oliver are on holiday in Spain.

My stepson, Myles, has just moved jobs to significant promotion and achieved one of his ambitions in life – bought his first BMW.

My stepdaughter, Philippa, has received excellent results from her assignments at University.

Mave, my wife's hand is swollen, she's upset because her skin is changing and under medical investigation for another problem and needs an operation soon!

My weight is steady – no significant loss!

THOUGHT FOR THE DAY
Life goes on – doesn't it just!! Who's writing this script? Who needs Oscars?

07.03.2006   Day 166

How can I stop myself feeling the pain, the hurt inside, the fear and concern for my children? How can I protect myself from the disappointments and the mistakes they make? Perhaps I am too close. Perhaps I love them too much. Perhaps I haven't let them go. Perhaps I should say no

THOUGHT FOR THE DAY
The price of parenthood.

08.03.2006   Day 167

Sir Nigel Crisp, the Chief Executive of our National Health Service, has retired early or resigned or got out to let someone more appropriate take on the health service reform? Depends which analyst you believe – on one hand record amounts of investment, patients never had it so good, more treatment, less waits – on the other hand, most of the money gone into salary/contract costs and one in four health organisations are in significant debt, ie spending money it hasn't got.

We are one of them – forecasting £24million debt this year. The consequences? Staff pushed to the limits, vacancy freeze, high staff sickness. Are patients safe? Yesterday – I was at a meeting and we were doing an urgent risk assessment because of inappropriate staff cover and dirty wards/clinics. Patients are increasingly at risk despite record amounts of investment!

Some say the reforms need time to bed in and work through, some say they are rushed, not thought through and fundamentally wrong. In the meantime, the managers do the best they can. Today, I am helping two of these organisations come together as one – merger – marriage? Is bigger better? More efficient? Can I broker this relationship?

Where bigger is definitely not better is ourselves. It's strange how perception of your body changes. At 17½ stone – I looked big and healthy and strutted around without a care in the world (denial) – now 2 stone lighter – I can grab Fatmea with both hands, massage my love handles and flabby middle with a recognition of how seriously fat I am.

I read recently about body dimorphic dysfunction – where a beauty queen (came second in Miss World & UK Competition) was obsessively worried about how ugly she was! A type of anorexia I guess. The point is – we are not our body image. We are what we are inside. Losing weight must come from within in order for it to be sustainable and healthy. We also need to love and celebrate our bodies, massage the flab, stroke the skin, acknowledge the parts of you, be whole.

THOUGHT FOR THE DAY
Look and listen beyond the surface – what do you experience?

09.03.2006   Day 168

A successful day yesterday – might even have made a difference! One of the questions I asked the group I was working with was – in everything you are expected to achieve in the next six months, where are you most vulnerable and what support do you need? The group handled this well – and an open discussion about risk, and team work developed.

This is also a good question to ask myself. Where or when am I most vulnerable? After an event/day like yesterday – successful hard work, long drive home – no work the following day – get the wine out – one glass or bottle too many!! Then came the crisps and the nuts!! An old response to an old situation. I must find an alternative way of relaxing, celebrating having fun. What support do I need? Ask my wife to help – perhaps challenge me at these times and not collude.

THOUGHT FOR THE DAY
Success creates vulnerability. Success means knowing when and where to get support and asking for it.

10.03.2006   Day 169

I did a little Tai Chi and learned some exercises with a Chi Ball yesterday. These are great ways of getting in touch with your body. Gentle, focussed and aimed at rebalancing inner strength and relaxation. I have managed to do about 30 minutes aerobic exercise most days on my cross trainer, but I think 30 minutes yoga and meditation would be good too. Making this a priority and planning in time will be a challenge. I need a space to do this – physical as well as mental. Good intentions – let's see!

THOUGHT FOR THE DAY
Exercise mind, body and spirit – let the Chi flow.

11.03.2006   Day 170

We used to run facilitator training for managers in a UK telecoms company – this is about 20 years ago. The training at that time was quite radical and intensive. The idea was to help them develop a style that was more in keeping with a team leader / coach as opposed to the most common style of command, control, dictate. This required a lot of exercises and feedback over a full week on a residential event, usually in a hotel near London. I remember one man in particular who needed a little support afterwards as he had one of these instant insights into himself. He suddenly realised that he had never listened all his life. He discovered that he would hear words, make assumptions, then control any conversation or situation from his perspective. This sudden 'aha' moment occurred after dinner one night and he just broke down in tears, saying how awful he was – he has been an idiot all his life, it's a wonder he's still married, what people must think about him behind his back!

This man had one big blind spot – and he discovered it in a drastic way. We had a couple of days left with him to help him assimilate his new insight and a few weeks after the course, we spoke again. He was very upbeat and told how he had to work to convince his wife he was not having an affair because she couldn't work out why he was so much nicer.

We all have blind spots – those things about ourselves that we can't see because we are too close to it and it takes either a significant learning experience or someone else telling you or showing you an aspect of yourself that you are oblivious to.

THOUGHT FOR THE DAY
What are my blind spots? Who or what will help me discover them? How do I create circumstances where I can learn and grow?

12.03 – 16.03.2006   Day 171 – 172 (Hong Kong)

17.03.2006   Day 173

I have just returned from a weeks' work in Hong Kong. It seems strange that since I have stopped looking for work, my reputation has spread. The work I have now nearly completed in Europe has gone down so well that the senior manager has been talking to her colleagues in Japan, Singapore, Bangkok and others who are now asking for the same sort of approach to development.

I think what has happened is that as I become clearer as to who I am, my purpose and the choices I make, the clearer I am in my delivery of management / leadership programmes. I start at you and the organisation, then, to you and your team, then, to you. It is the focus on the personal and its impact on everything else that seems to be powerful. I can only do this if I am doing the same.

The shift in my 'philosophy' to work over the last few years has not been to seek it out but to concentrate on what I am doing in the sense of real presence, real questions, real challenge without any agenda to sell or search for more work, but to do what intuitively feels right for my client. Also, to be clearer about the type of work that I want to do – I turned down several requests in Hong Kong this week – why? I couldn't hear the 'personal questions' – I heard 'quick fix and cheapest way' – which is not the business I am in.

Besides one over indulgent night – which was the first night catching up with an old friend, drowning our sorrows watching a painfully miserable England performance against France rugby union – the rest was moderation.

I feel Fatmea is well under control and has now reduced in just over 5 months by 35lbs. I don't weigh myself that often now – I have this inner confidence that eventually I will achieve my ideal weight – I will know this somehow in myself not what the books tell me. I feel I have some way to go yet and it may take me another six months – this is OK – the important thing is that the value of knowing who you are, the discipline of reflection and personal challenge to be conscious in every moment and the belief that you have real choice about achieving what's important – these are the real elements of successful weight loss.

THOUGHT FOR THE DAY
It's not how far you travel that's important – it's what you do on the way that makes the difference.

18.03.2006   Day 174

Woke up this morning early. Jet lag still influencing sleep patterns – feeling a little sad and wondering what that was about. Concern about my wife's health, concerns about my sons' situation, concern about a speeding fine (caught on camera) I can't believe or remember speeding, concerns about my non-executive responsibilities at work – so what's going on?

These are all things I have no (or very little) control over – apart from me deciding how I react to them. So, react positively, honestly and in a supportive and, if appropriate, a challenging way when and if they become reality in the moment, in my immediate conscious reality. So, move on, enjoy the moment, enjoy the day, listen to and experience the beauty of the moment – don't get lost in the negative things that might never happen!

THOUGHT FOR THE DAY
Focus less on those things you can't control, focus more on those things you can.

19.03.2006　Day 175

Who or what is my God? My God is the infinite and superior intelligence which is interwoven in every speck of this universe and in every heart of every thing in existence. It is a force for good and when we pray, we tap into this force increasing our chances of realising some of this force is our expression as loving human beings.

Jesus knew and believed this, other great religious leaders also believed this - their leadership was significant because they were messengers of God, bringing this force of good to the masses, making it accessible to everyone.

Ultimately, I believe the point of all religions is to help us realise our full potential as human beings. This potential manifested in our ability to give and receive love. To forgive and heal ourselves and others. To be conscious in every moment, to choose to be true to ourselves, be genuine and not hide behind a mask of ego or status.

I also believe in an afterlife - energy does not disappear - it is transformed. The energy of our physical self becomes part of the organic matter of this earth, but our spiritual selves, ie: that part which is not physical, our soul, the essence of who we are lives on. It lives on either through the eyes and hearts of living loved ones, through another being born again, or floats in the ether between earthly existence and the spirit world, or elements of all of these. No one can prove the above - you either believe it or not. There are many events, miracles, sightings, recollections under hypnosis and other strange occurrences that can not be explained unless you begin to believe in something.

Having faith is believing that there is more to this life than what we allow ourselves to experience. Some use a religious structure to help focus on a path towards enlightenment or heaven, some meditate, and some just live it every moment.

To transform our bodily selves and realise full health, I believe we have to dig deep and ask what we truly believe. Having faith helps, if you don't then just believe in the beauty of humanity, believe in yourself and celebrate who you are. This will, in itself, be your religion and help you towards health and happiness - the ultimate goal for us all.

I am a child of the Universe, a mere speck in the great scheme of things yet powerful in realising how I connect.

20.03.2006   Day 176

3 year anniversary of the invasion of Baghdad. Over two thousand American and British soldiers killed, thousands of Iraqis and over 60 Iraqis a day dying now. The prime minister of Iraq is describing it as a civil war, the west is claiming we are helping them stabilise and to form a democracy. Sunni is against Shiite and many ordinary Iraqi civilians live in fear behind closed doors. Is this the necessary painful transition to forming an independent safe, democratic Iraq, or was it a huge mistake? Is the world safer as a consequence – will it ever be?

Some Professor on TV was interviewed yesterday claiming all religions are virus' of the mind and dangerous. What he was really saying was that 'blind faith' can be used to justify actions directed to terrorism and war. This is when it is dangerous and the meaning of religion should be understood and not acted upon blindly, it shouldn't give anyone a divine right of power over anyone else. I agree – there is no one right religion and we should all live in harmony and have compassion for each other.

To do this requires forgiveness and letting go of all grievances – taking hate and anger out of our hearts. This is, I know, is difficult but at least the world should know there is a path to peace (and it does not involve the weapons of war).

Where I disagree with the professor is that you can have blind faith for the good – some people are totally dedicated to the worship of God and hope and pray for the good of humanity. If blind faith works for them, then why challenge it? To them, it may not be blind – only to others who don't fully understand or appreciate the depth and passion one can have for ones faith.

It's when the depth and passion overspills to attack itself when it becomes dangerous, externalising the negative emotion in the judgement of others.

I watched a film on the plane coming back from Hong Kong last week – I wanted to turn it off after half way through but forced myself to watch Jarhead – essentially a film about training the American soldier for the Gulf War. To me it demonstrated a dehumanising process to get young men into a state where they could, without hesitation, follow order to kill another human being. In the end, there was very little human to human contact as most deaths were by air and missiles. I know this has been the process of training for years and I don't know another way to prepare for the brutality and inhumanity of war. It still makes me feel sick to see what we can do to each other.

Someone has published a book called the 'Yob Culture' – it's a sorry testimony of the state of our society as it describes mindless attacks from gangs of youths violently impacting the lives of innocent people. It has become endemic! There are times when I feel ashamed of being part of the human race! It's easy to get drawn into the dark side – and at these times, I have to remind myself of the beauty and miracles of life. It seems too passive – surely we can do something to counteract the 'world yob culture'? The world needs healing.

THOUGHT FOR THE DAY
I pray that Iraq rediscovers its greatness and becomes a model of healing for us all.

21.03.2006   Day 177

I am close to finishing this diary. I will finish at a time I know the battle of my bulge – the Farewell to Fatmea is almost won. She will always be there but a mere shadow of her former self. It will take probably another 6 months to reach a weight I am happy with.

The important thing is not to loose momentum, not to give up, to continually remind myself of the principles of self healing and the journey towards discovery of who I really am. Today I remind myself to:

- judge less of others, it's a waste of energy, may falsely make me feel superior or better but it serves no real purpose
- really pay attention and listen to those whom I come into

contact with, ask myself the purpose of the contact and look for adding value to the moment – give freely

- forgive myself and others for things in the past as these were done out of limited awareness and limited awareness of the true consequences
- stand back, look at yourself, become your own guardian angel – remind yourself you have real choice in every moment
- choose humility over status and ego
- choose a long, healthy and active life
- focus on those things you can control, not on the things you can't
- recognise how I am creating this moment in time – sense how I connect to what's happening now – stay awake / alert to the coincidences and messages for me and my journey
- love yourself, love another, receive love
- believe in the power to heal ourselves and others

THOUGHT FOR THE DAY
How can my presence add value to the day?

22.03.2006   Day 178

I make mistakes, misjudge, give in to comfort eating and drinking, forget who I am, loose my sense of awareness, get frustrated, fearful, impatient, feel guilty, regretful, sad and angry about the past – I am human! This diary is no magic wand! It is a record of my life in 6 months and an insight into my struggle for weight loss and healthy body, mind and spirit. My journey will continue and my writings will change – but I must, on a daily basis, remind myself.

THOUGHT FOR THE DAY
Just when you think you've got it – something hits you to remind you – you're not there yet – keep going!

23.03.2006   Day 179

Do you believe in fate? I think I do – to a certain extent. It should be simple, but I also believe to a large extent we are master of our destiny. We are dealt a certain deck of cards, our DNA, genetic make up, our biological inheritance. Our first years of life are shaped significantly by our parents or carers. After that – what happens? Do we shape events or are they pre-scripted for us to walk into? What happens, I believe, is dependent on the choices we make throughout life, therefore we are masters – but is there something else going on that influences us to make a choice in a certain way? Why have things turned out like this? So many complex, interwoven sets of circumstances has resulted in me being here right now. What for? What's the deal? Is there a reason? What's my purpose? I can not answer these questions fully right now, but I suspect they are healthy questions to reflect on from time to time.

Someone said to me when I was a lot younger 'Mike, there is a reason you are experiencing these events, this is preparation for greater things that lay ahead!'. At the time, I didn't acknowledge the sentiment, now I think my life has been, in a sense, an apprenticeship and I am still to graduate – I still have much to learn. My cap and gown will have to wait a little longer.

THOUGHT FOR THE DAY
Maybe, just maybe what you choose to do right now will influence the rest of your life and impact on many others.

24.03.2006   Day 180

The final entry!

It's been an amazing six months!! What started as a simple record of thoughts and feelings in my quest to lose weight has turned into a mind, body and spiritual process of renewal and hope.

Weight loss in this period has been a total of 35lbs, or 2½ stone! This has not been difficult and I have eaten what I want.

The key is knowing what you want! Knowing what's possible and choosing to get it!

I still have some way to go for I suspect a healthy weight for me is 200lbs, or 14 stone, 4lbs. The secret is to continue on my overall journey of self discovery, keeping my guardian angel close and not being a victim to circumstance.

So, the journey continues and whilst I travel I pray

Give me the courage to face the truth
Give me the compassion to let go of the past
Give me hope for peace in the future
Give me the awareness for happiness right now!!

2. A Journey of Happiness

A Journey to Happiness

Introduction

The following is a reflective exercise using symbols within a fantasy journey. It introduces the key elements of happiness summarised in Section 3 – 'The Wheel of Happiness'. It requires an open mind, quiet personal space and time to think deeply about what any of this means to you. None of this is meant to be prescriptive – just an invitation to explore and discover for yourself what makes you happy.

Imagine yourself taking this journey. Whilst reading this account of your quest; relax, put some soothing music on quietly in the background (for some people, this may be distracting – so only put on if it helps), avoid distractions like the phone and other people. Breathe deeply several times before beginning and during pauses or rests on your journey. Read slowly and try to see the images, visualise them in your own mind.

Now, take a deep breath and read slowly – try and picture the images in your mind.

Waking up from a deep sleep, you decide to get there – where?

You are unsure, but you know deep down it's time to change. Slowly and methodically, you begin to prepare for your journey. As you do, you begin to notice things more – birds singing, the noise of traffic or passers by, and the rustle of leaves in the wind.

It feels strange preparing to go away, unsure where you are going, yet there is an air of confidence in you that what you are about to do is the right thing.

You decide only to take a bottle of water with you for refreshment on the way, as something tells you that you will be well nourished on this journey. You find an old bottle and decide to fill it with tap water. As the water fills the bottle, you notice its clear sparkling qualities, you let it overflow and feel its cold trickle through your hands and you catch the mirror of reflection it offers and you realise – at that moment – this is water of life.

With rucksack on your back to carry the water, you realise now is the time to go.

Slowly, opening your front door you begin to realise that somehow, you are about to step into another world.

You breathe deeply, relax and take that first step. Immediately, you realise you are in another world; a world of green rolling hills with ice capped mountains in the distance, the sky is a deep blue with a few white puffy clouds hanging lightly, the birds are singing, the air is fresh yet warm and everything around you is inviting you to walk on, walk through the fields towards the highest peak.

There seems to be a vague path through the grass up ahead and you stride confidently towards it, feeling the soft grass give way beneath your feet and brushing aside the tall grass and bushes as you walk through. The smell of wild flowers and the beautiful sound of the bird harmony already gives you a sense of wellbeing and confidence that this is the right way.

Up ahead, you see two people, one small child and an older person crouching over with a walking stick. The child seems to be helping the older person walk along the path.

You approach and ask "Hello, are you OK? Do you need a hand?"

"Do you have a drink?" says the child.

"Only water – but you're welcome to have some."

The child gives the older person a drink and hands it back. "Thank you" says the older person "I would like to give you this in return."

"That's not necessary, please, no – I expect nothing in return."

"Please, I insist." And with that – the older person puts into your hand an 'hour glass' – the yellow sand running swiftly through from end to end.

"Thank you" you reply, "please, tell me your names?"

The child replies "Memory", the older person "Fantasy" and they both say together "we do not exist." And walk away.

You watch them for a while, and see them slowly disappear, becoming indistinguishable from the trees and rocks.

The hour glass you put in your rucksack, continuing your journey, wondering what you will do with a 'timer'.

After a while walking through meadows, you come to a beautiful valley with steep sided cliffs and rocks reflecting different colours in the sun.

At the end of this valley, you see something glistening, shining in the sun, like a mirror catching a sunbeam and flashing in your eyes. As you approach, it becomes clear that there is a person sat regally upon a rock, on their head is a crown of gold and jewels, he holds a gold staff and is dressed in a gold cloak.

You approach with awe and anticipation, wondering whether you should bow or kneel.

"Halt, who goes there?" says the majestic figure.

"Only I, a humble traveller."

"This is my land, I say who goes or not. How much can you pay?"

"I carry no money, only water and an hour glass"

"I have no need for an hour glass, I have many time pieces. Give me some of your water and you can pass."

As you hand over your bottle of water, he takes it with his hands which are adorned with jewelled rings and you notice, as you get closer, that the gold on his crown is tainted and the embroidery on his gown is torn.

"Here, let me give you this in return."

"Oh no, please, I don't need anything."

"I insist!"

And with that, he hands you a small bag containing a few gold coins.

"That's very generous of you."

"Not really, I have mountains of them – don't you think that's splendid?"

"Yes, and thank you" you say, leaving and slightly bowing as you return to your journey, placing the bag of coins carefully in your rucksack.

You can't help noticing a hint of sadness in his voice and an air of melancholy about him – was he happy?

The scenery changes – the open meadows and valleys are left behind and a growing density of trees create many shadows as the sun struggles to dance through the tall trees and swaying branches.

You sense something is not quite right, as if the woods have eyes and you are trespassing. Then – *thump!* You are knocked over by a scruffy looking man who then begins to demand your rucksack, pulling and tearing at it. You fight back, lashing out with your fists and feet shouting "No, no!"

You get angry and land a strong blow across his chin. He staggers, struggles to get up and runs into the woods. You are shaken, shocked, then wonder what makes someone so desperate to attack a humble traveller such as yourself? You hope you didn't hurt him too badly.

You continue your journey, and after a short while, you turn a corner and become aware of a figure lying in the road. It is the man you fought earlier. He looks hurt, you approach with caution. He has blood coming from his mouth. You take your water bottle, clean his mouth and give him a drink, staying with him until he is able to sit up. He says sorry, you reply "I'm sorry too."

"Here, this is all I have. Please take it." The beggar takes, from his neck, a rope with a small name plate – saying simply 'John'. "Please take this, your kindness has saved me."

"I can not, this is too much."

"No – I insist, it's important for you to have it."

You take it with a suspicion that these gifts were meant for you in some way. Helping you on your journey.

Once your new found friend is fully recovered, you swap stories, shake hands and bid farewell. The woods continue on for sometime, then the shape of the trees changes from the tall, imposing statue like forest, to shorter, thorny bushes, spread out more. The ground was getting rougher with little grass and the weather had turned a little colder. A mist begins to form and your path becomes uncertain, and you wonder what will happen next. You realise how hungry you have become and are beginning to be a little wary about the road ahead.

There's a rustle in the bushes ahead, there's a screeching noise above. You look up - an eagle soars close by. The rustle ahead gets louder, a low rumbling sound, a movement - you freeze. You are face to face with a lion; a glorious beast, standing tall, head held high, lean, and muscular, its coat smooth with a velvet sheen.

It stares and looks straight at you. The eagle then soars down - it carries a branch of leaves in its claws. The eagle lands on the lion - they both move forward - should you run or stay?

What does this mean?

The eagle swoops towards you, dropping the branch at your feet. You pick it up - the eagle and lion stare - something tells you that things happen for a reason, they appeared because you were hungry and scared.

You take the leaves from the branch and taste them. They immediately give you a feeling of warmth and satisfaction. The eagle soars away and the lion strides off into the mist. You reflect on how these great animals are fit to live, eat to live and are masters in their own domain and free to roam.

Taking the branch, with the few remaining leaves on, you place it in your rucksack with the hour glass, bag of gold and John's nameplate, and, of course, your precious water bottle.

The journey continues, and you begin to relax more, breathe deeply and you sense the fascination in the changing scenery as now, the snow capped mountain peaks become clearer.

The snow glistens in the sun and you begin to climb steadily, admiring the mountain plants growing from the rocks and glancing back to see the green meadows and valley. In the distance the forest trees now appear as a mass of green carpet. You wonder whether the child and old person do exist, if the King of the Pass will ever be happy and whether John will survive. Knowing you now have nourishment kindly given by the lion and eagle, you begin to climb with confidence.

After a while, you see a small child, picking wild flowers which are growing amongst the rocks. You say hello, she smiles and continues to pick her flowers. Her eyes are large and bluey-green, her hair is blonde and long, she conveys a sense of vulnerability and you wonder – why is she here on her own?

"Can I help you little girl?"

"I don't need help to pick flowers, but if you have anything to eat or drink, I would be grateful."

You offer some leaves from your branch and water from your bottle.

She eats and drinks heartily.

"Thank you" and she gives you her flowers.

You accept, they are wild, colourful and scented with such sweet perfume. The petals are perfectly open and their lines of nature visible to the keen observer.

She then throws her arms around you, hugs you and kisses you on your cheek and says "thank you".

Her eyes are full of tears, yet she smiles. You take a deep breath – that moment – you knew – you were loved. She skipped off down the mountain shouting "Bye!"

This indeed is a curious journey. You carefully wrap the flowers together with a piece of twine and place them in your rucksack with the other precious gifts.

You are unsure of the time and sense it is getting a little late in the afternoon, but somehow, time isn't a concern – the journey continues and you climb further up the mountain side. The air is getting fresher and a little colder and you are beginning to get a real sense of isolation. The scene of meadows and forest were, by now, long left behind and facing you now was a steep climb up mountain paths. You take a deep breath.

You had just finished climbing a particularly difficult incline and you enter what looks like a dead end. Exploring these steep walls around you, you notice in the corner a small opening. Through this opening, you can see a way forward. It is almost like entering another world. Landscaped gardens, fountains, a running stream, fruit trees and tropical plants of all colours and shapes. In the middle of this garden is a large oak tree under which is sitting a young man reading a book.

You approach with eagerness to know what this place is – "Hello, what are you reading?"

"It's my life!"

"How can you read about your life – you're so young and you haven't lived it yet?"

"I know – I'm learning about my life."

"And the answers are in that book?"

"They will be when I write it."

"Oh, that's interesting, you're reading a book you haven't read yet."

"I'm still learning."

You are confused – you exchange stories, some water and some leaves to eat. You begin to wonder what there is to learn about being in this garden and talking to the auto biographer. As you gesture to leave, shaking hands, he gives you a book – entitled "My Life". You open it – blank pages! Apart from the title of the first chapter – "What I have learnt on my journey so far". You know then, that this is an offer to care for your mind, your thoughts, your learning and growth – as a garden. Your journey is now fuelled with excitement, anticipating recording your tales and stories so far to a readership as yet unknown. You get lost in your thoughts, and before you know it – you have a sense of being lost. Again, you are in mountainous terrain, ahead of you there seems to be a plateaux with what looks like a stretch of water, river or lake. You believe that's where you should be heading, but looking around you, you can not get a sense of where next.

Then you hear "Roll up, roll up, bargains galore – here you can have what you want or what you need!"

A booming voice, the sort of which you would hear in any busy market place was coming from behind a clump of rocks beyond the bushes ahead. This you had to explore. And sure enough – the market stall, the seller and his wares!

"What are you selling?" you ask.

"What do you want? Here we have food of all sorts, designed to give you pleasure, and here we have whatever you need – designed to make you happy!"

"But there's nothing on this side of the stall – how can nothing make you happy?"

"Some people need nothing to make them happy."

You are confused, and glance over to the mouth-watering selection of foods, which happen to be your favourite. "Surely pleasure is happiness?"

"Not necessarily" the market seller replies "please eat what you want for a pleasant experience, it's your choice! Do you want to be satisfied and lost, or hungry and found?"

You then knew to focus on what you needed, and not what you wanted – and immediately, the market seller hands you a compass – with one directional arrow pointing "this way".

"Thank you – can I offer you this bag of gold in return?"

"No, I have no need for gold, but a drink of water will quench my thirst."

The compass you hold and follow on your next step of the journey. You sense it is close to the end, or is it the beginning?

The path takes you around the mountainside, the views are breathtaking, below you could see the eagle soaring, and you can almost touch the puffy clouds in the blue sky. Once you have carefully navigated your way around the mountainside, the land opened up and again you are into green fields, in the distance you can see a river and beyond the river, what looks like a small town. This, you know, is home and that's where you want to be. You approach someone standing there – you know this person to be a 'teacher', not in the school sense – but in the sense of the person that will help you in the moment now.

"What is your quest?" says the teacher.

"I want to cross the river to go home"

"You may cross, using the 54 steps there to guide you, but first, what gifts do you have for me?"

"I have water."

"What else?"

You begin to empty your rucksack.

First is the 'timer' – but the sand has frozen – no longer flowing.

Second is the bag of gold – but the gold has turned to dust.

Third is John's nameplate – but the name has changed to 'peace'

Fourth is the branch with nourishing leaves – and it has more leaves on.

Fifth is the wild flowers – as fresh as the day they were picked and smelling beautiful.

Sixth is the journal – already with writing on the first page.

Seventh is the compass – this time with the words 'you have arrived' written on it.

The teacher smiles.

"Thank you for these gifts – please proceed over the 54 steps. You may take as long as you like. Each step has a meaning, for some are more relevant than others – you choose which ones to step on and in what sequence. You may not need them all. On the other side of the river, you will find what you are looking for."

You thank the teacher and with careful first steps, begin to experience your way across the river. The river flowed steadily, it's blue glaze giving a sense of hypnotic movement. Night turned to day, day turned to night, and the sun rose in its yellow splendour and settled, drinking in its red glory. The stars sparkled in rapid mystery and the moon bathed its ward in shadows. Each step you took gave you strength - a deep conviction that you are now almost there.

The final steps.

You arrive on the other side, you turn, wave with a sense of gratitude to your teacher. In front of you is a water mill, its seven white sails turn silently driven by a continuous flow of water. The water wheel turns, moves with eternal energy.

You lay down, you know this is home. You breathe deeply, relax and reflect on the gifts you gained, the gifts you gave away and the steps you have taken. Welcome home.

3. The Wheel of Happiness

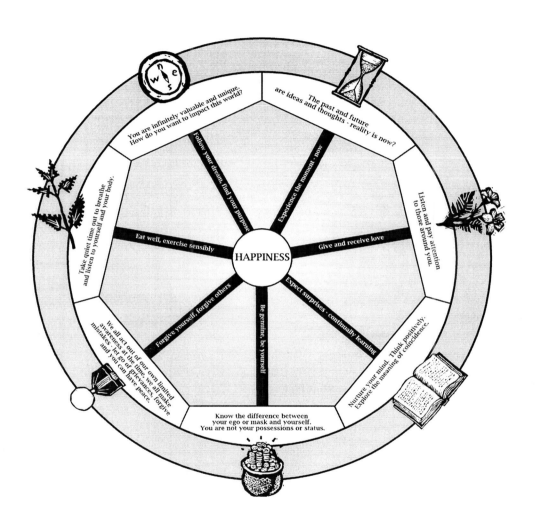

You are infinitely valuable and unique. How do you want to impact this world?

The past and future are ideas and thoughts - reality is now?

Follow your dream, find your purpose

Experience the moment - now

Take quiet time out to breathe and listen to yourself and your body.

Listen and pay attention to those around you.

Eat well, exercise sensibly

HAPPINESS

Give and receive love

Forgive yourself, forgive others

Be genuine, be yourself

Expect surprises - continually learning

We all act out of our own limited awareness at the time; we all make mistakes. let go of grievances. forgive and you can have peace.

Nurture your mind. Think positively. Explore the meaning of coincidence.

Know the difference between your ego or mask and yourself. You are not your possessions or status.

4. 54 Steps to Happiness

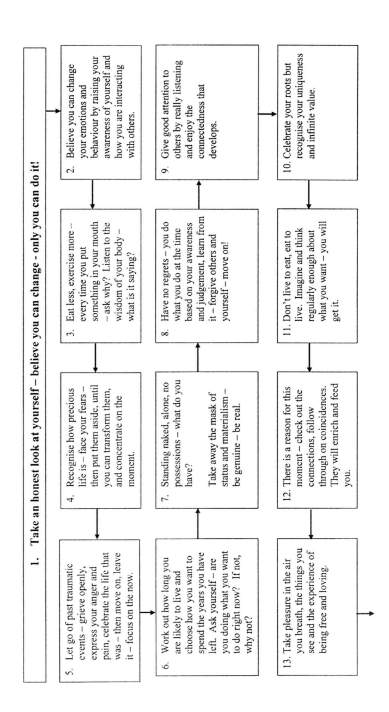

1. **Take an honest look at yourself – believe you can change – only you can do it!**

2. Believe you can change your emotions and behaviour by raising your awareness of yourself and how you are interacting with others.

3. Eat less, exercise more – every time you put something in your mouth – ask why? Listen to the wisdom of your body – what is it saying?

4. Recognise how precious life is – face your fears – then put them aside, until you can transform them, and concentrate on the moment.

5. Let go of past traumatic events – grieve openly, express your anger and pain, celebrate the life that was – then move on, leave it – focus on the now.

6. Work out how long you are likely to live and choose how you want to spend the years you have left. Ask yourself – are you doing what you want to do right now? If not, why not?

7. Standing naked, alone, no possessions – what do you have?

   Take away the mask of status and materialism – be genuine – be real.

8. Have no regrets – you do what you do at the time based on your awareness and judgement, learn from it – forgive others and yourself – move on!

9. Give good attention to others by really listening and enjoy the connectedness that develops.

10. Celebrate your roots but recognise your uniqueness and infinite value.

11. Don't live to eat, eat to live. Imagine and think regularly enough about what you want – you will get it.

12. There is a reason for this moment – check out the connections, follow through on coincidences. They will enrich and feed you.

13. Take pleasure in the air you breath, the things you see and the experience of being free and loving.

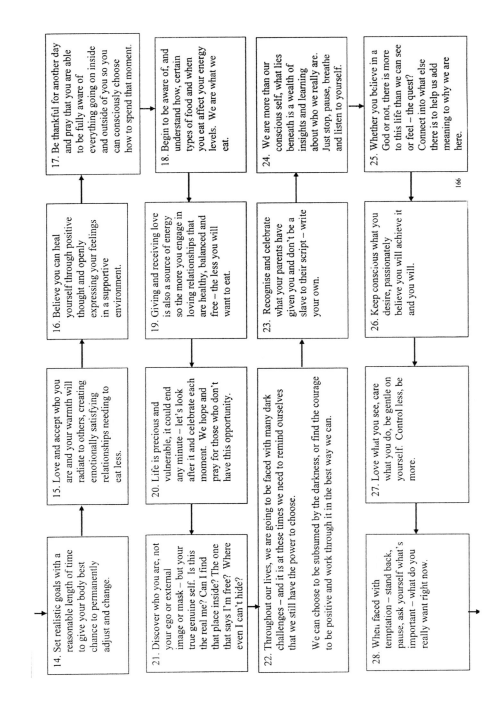

14. Set realistic goals with a reasonable length of time to give your body best chance to permanently adjust and change.

15. Love and accept who you are and your warmth will radiate to others, creating emotionally satisfying relationships needing to eat less.

16. Believe you can heal yourself through positive thought and openly expressing your feelings in a supportive environment.

17. Be thankful for another day and pray that you are able to be fully aware of everything going on inside and outside of you so you can consciously choose how to spend that moment.

18. Begin to be aware of, and understand how, certain types of food and when you eat affect your energy levels. We are what we eat.

19. Giving and receiving love is also a source of energy so the more you engage in loving relationships that are healthy, balanced and free – the less you will want to eat.

20. Life is precious and vulnerable, it could end any minute – let's look after it and celebrate each moment. We hope and pray for those who don't have this opportunity.

21. Discover who you are, not your ego or external image or mask – but your true genuine self. Is this the real me? Can I find that place inside? The one that says I'm free? Where even I can't hide?

22. Throughout our lives, we are going to be faced with many dark challenges – and it is at these times we need to remind ourselves that we still have the power to choose.

We can choose to be subsumed by the darkness, or find the courage to be positive and work through it in the best way we can.

23. Recognise and celebrate what your parents have given you and don't be a slave to their script – write your own.

24. We are more than our conscious self, what lies beneath is a wealth of insights and learning about who we really are. Just stop, pause, breathe and listen to yourself.

25. Whether you believe in a God or not, there is more to this life than we can see or feel – the quest? Connect into what else there is to help us add meaning to why we are here.

26. Keep conscious what you desire, passionately believe you will achieve it and you will.

27. Love what you see, care what you do, be gentle on yourself. Control less, be more.

28. When faced with temptation – stand back, pause, ask yourself what's important – what do you really want right now.

166

236

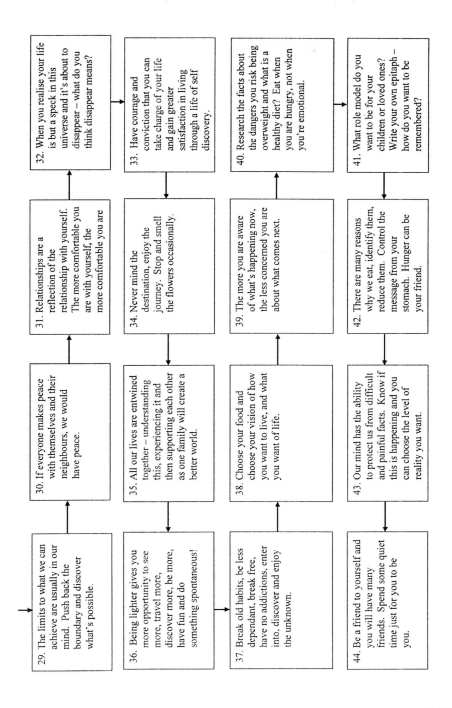

29. The limits to what we can achieve are usually in our mind. Push back the boundary and discover what's possible.

30. If everyone makes peace with themselves and their neighbours, we would have peace.

31. Relationships are a reflection of the relationship with yourself. The more comfortable you are with yourself, the more comfortable you are

32. When you realise your life is but a speck in this universe and it's about to disappear – what do you think disappear means?

33. Have courage and conviction that you can take charge of your life and gain greater satisfaction in living through a life of self discovery.

34. Never mind the destination, enjoy the journey. Stop and smell the flowers occasionally.

35. All our lives are entwined together – understanding this, experiencing it and then supporting each other as one family will create a better world.

36. Being lighter gives you more opportunity to see more, travel more, discover more, be more, have fun and do something spontaneous!

37. Break old habits, be less dependant, break free, have no addictions, enter into, discover and enjoy the unknown.

38. Choose your food and choose your vision of how you want to live, and what you want of life.

39. The more you are aware of what's happening now, the less concerned you are about what comes next.

40. Research the facts about the dangers you risk being overweight and what is a healthy diet? Eat when you are hungry, not when you're emotional.

41. What role model do you want to be for your children or loved ones? Write your own epitaph – how do you want to be remembered?

42. There are many reasons why we eat, identify them, reduce them. Control the message from your stomach. Hunger can be your friend.

43. Our mind has the ability to protect us from difficult and painful facts. Know if this is happening and you can choose the level of reality you want.

44. Be a friend to yourself and you will have many friends. Spend some quiet time just for you to be you.

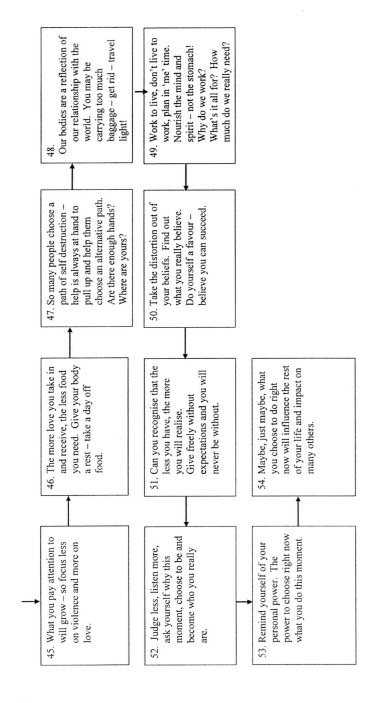

45. What you pay attention to will grow – so focus less on violence and more on love.

46. The more love you take in and receive, the less food you need. Give your body a rest – take a day off food.

47. So many people choose a path of self destruction – help is always at hand to pull up and help them choose an alternative path. Are there enough hands? Where are yours?

48. Our bodies are a reflection of our relationship with the world. You may be carrying too much baggage – get rid – travel light!

49. Work to live, don't live to work, plan in 'me' time. Nourish the mind and spirit – not the stomach! Why do we work? What's it all for? How much do we really need?

50. Take the distortion out of your beliefs. Find out what you really believe. Do yourself a favour – believe you can succeed.

51. Can you recognise that the less you have, the more you will realise. Give freely without expectations and you will never be without.

52. Judge less, listen more, ask yourself why this moment, choose to be and become who you really are.

53. Remind yourself of your personal power. The power to choose right now what you do this moment.

54. Maybe, just maybe, what you choose to do right now will influence the rest of your life and impact on many others.

5. The Slimmed Down Version

The 'Slimmed Down' version

- Accept and recognise you have a problem and only you can solve it
- Take a long hard look in the mirror at your naked self – and ask - is this what you want?
- Eat less, exercise more
- Recognise that you can change the way you think and feel
- It's not what you eat, it's how much – check out the portions
- Understand why you eat – stop eating and drinking for emotional reasons
- List and understand the consequences of being overweight
- Take control of your eating habits – be conscious when you eat
- Recognise and face your fears
- Understand there are no short cuts – this is a life long journey
- Stop living in the past, let go of grief and regret
- Forgive yourself and others
- Be clear about how you want to spend the rest of your life – healthy or unhealthy
- Believe that you have the power to choose
- Recognise the difference between 'you' and your 'ego'
- Think less about food and more about life
- Ask yourself when you catch yourself judging and criticising others whether this in fact is an aspect of your own behaviour you dislike
- Recognise the physical feeling of being full – this means stop eating!

- Ask yourself – what's your purpose in life and are you fit enough to achieve it?
- Ask yourself – do you eat to live or live to eat?!
- Every time you think of food – remind yourself of what you really want in life
- Use it or lose it
- Love the miracle of you
- Express how you feel more often
- Check out coincidences and ask what is its meaning
- We are what we eat, we are what we think
- Check out how types of food effect our energy
- How can we listen to our bodies' wisdom
- People are dying now every second in horrendous circumstances – life is precious –celebrate what we have
- Our mind and body are inseparable – they are one
- Record your dreams and interpret them yourself
- Stop being busy – stop – be still – listen. What do you hear?
- Be aware in the moment and passionate about the desire for achievement of health – mind, body and soul
- Know what you want in life
- Control less, give more
- Accept who you are, make peace with yourself and others
- Whenever faced with temptation, pause, breathe deeply and consider – what's really important in your life right now?
- Our relationships are a reflection of the relationship with ourselves
- Make a contract with your God – get to know each other
- Imagine yourself looking at your gravestone – what would you want it to say?
- Face up to your own mortality – the life you have left
- Take charge of your life – seek greater satisfaction in living through a journey of self discovery
- Making a difference to me – then you
- Never mind the destination, enjoy the journey – stop and smell the flowers occasionally
- Do I live to work or work to live? How much do I really need?
- Wake up to the connections all around you now!
- To lighten up, you have to let go!

- Lose the weight, cry less, laugh more
- Forgive others, forgive yourself
- Show your children what works in life
- We are all from the same source, part of the same family
- Don't regret, you did what you could at the time – move on!
- The more aware you are of what's happening now, the less concerned you are about what comes next
- There are many reasons why we eat; identify them and reduce them
- How do you want to be remembered?
- Patience, persistence and a determination to succeed
- Be still and listen, be gentle with the powerful forces around you
- How can I realise the connection between us and maintain a real sense of presence?
- We can heal ourselves
- Drink less, think young, be merry on the spirit of humanity, not on the spirit of alcohol
- How can I listen to the wisdom of my body and act out of love?
- The more we are, the brighter we become, to lighten up what sometimes is a gloomy place
- None of us know what's round the corner, cherish what we have right now and celebrate the good times
- Eat less, drink less, be merry by really listening to those who love you and let the joy in your heart show
- Look long and deep enough and you can see the beauty in most things
- Cherish your mind and body – be fit
- Never loose hope for a better world
- Moderation
- Take less in and lighten up
- Recognise the choices you make in every moment
- A liver is for life, not just for Christmas
- Change or die
- Be still not boring, be quiet not loud
- Respect yourself will help you respect others
- Identify your distorted beliefs and change them

- Know what is enough
- Peace starts with me
- What does being real mean today?
- What is perfection if it is not now? The moment we cherish
- Find the courage before it's too late
- Those that have less often have more
- Lose weight, gain freedom and drink in the beauty around you
- The best things in life are free
- Don't put off til tomorrow what you can do or say today
- Recognising and understanding your weaknesses and vulnerability can be a strength
- What legacy do you want to leave?
- The more aware of the options we have the easier it is to choose
- Choose to be happy, choose to have fun, choose to be you
- Sometimes it's worth pausing a moment on your journey and checking where you actually are
- A days trauma can result in a life of misery and days of tears can lead to rediscovering joy
- Nurture your connections, explore their meaning, they all have a purpose
- Love yourself, love another and you will be loved
- What miracle will we witness today? Inspirational moments are all around us – can we experience them?
- Do yourself a favour – believe you can succeed!
- Simply this, this moment is now and is special
- Better to take your time when climbing up a mountain – you can pause, soak in the views and enjoy the pounding of your heart, the expansion of your lungs, the sense of achievement and the ever changing horizon
- Judge less, listen more, ask yourself why this moment, choose to be and become who you really are
- Imagine yourself thin, act as if you are and you will be
- Listen to your guardian angel, find the courage to choose to be free
- If you are able to dance, do so and be happy

- You face this moment now, deal with what's real, not with what might or might not happen
- Look and listen beyond the surface – what do you experience?
- Create circumstances where you can learn and grow, find ways of discovering your blind spots
- It's not how far you travel that's important, it's what you do on the way that makes a difference
- Focus less on those things you can't control, focus on those things you can
- Make your presence add value to the day
- Just when you think you've got it – something hits you to remind you – no, you're not there yet. Keep going!
- Maybe, just maybe, what you choose to do right now will influence the rest of your life and impact many others.

6. The Fundamentals of Healthy Eating

The Fundamentals of Healthy Eating

- Every time you put food or drink to your mouth – ask yourself why?
- Avoid the obvious 'fat' and 'sweet' foods
- Eat slowly, sitting down, consciously experience the moment
- Drink water before and during your meal
- Eat when you're hungry, not when you're emotional
- Identify your vulnerable times, the times when you are most likely to overindulge – call upon your guardian angel (observe yourself) – find an alternative activity
- Remember alcohol is food too – and the more you drink the less conscious / aware you become and the more vulnerable you are, hence the chances of overeating are greater
- Listen to your body, understand the signs of hunger – make it your friend and stop eating when you are nearly full
- Eat more fruit, vegetables, fish, white meat – less fat, red meat and carbohydrates
- Chew slowly, really taste the food. Enjoy it and understand and appreciate where it came from
- Avoid large portions and all-u-can eat situations – better to eat small, regularly, less in the morning and evening
- When you're hungry, recognise it, celebrate it and eat just enough to satisfy it and wait until next time you are hungry – do not be a slave to other people's eating times
- Exercise at least 30 minutes for 5 days a week. Get your heart and muscles working so they can burn the food you eat more efficiently.
- Avoid salty food – don't add extra salt.

7. The Basics of Light and Heavy Foods

The Basics of Light and Heavy Foods

Eat What you Want Of:	Foods in Moderation:	Foods to Avoid:
All vegetables	Potato	Anything deep fried
All fruit	Pasta	Pastry
Fish	Lightly fried in oil	Ice cream
Salad	Lean red meat	Sweets
White meat	Cheese	Crisps
Cereal (not sugary stuff)	Pizza	Nuts (some are OK)
Yogurt (without sweet stuff)	Milk	Butter
Love	Booze	Cakes
Hope	Rice	Donuts
Forgiveness	Bread	Sugar
Joy		Salt
Laughter		Hate
Fun		Greed
		Guilt
		Anger
		Regret

8. And Finally …

And Finally ...

Many of us feel deeply that we want to make a difference – we want our lives to mean something in the bigger scheme of life. While this is a noble motive, we might want to explore what lies at its root.

Does the drive to make a difference arise from ego's need to feel worthy? If my ego is not convinced that I matter, I may want visible proof that I do by making some kind of impact on life.

Soul doesn't need proof that it's worthy. Soul thrives on being awake and connected. Perhaps if we let go of the pressure we feel from our ego's need to be recognised, we will be more open and able to simply live soulfully. And by doing that, we WILL make a difference!

"A person's worth is contingent upon who he is, not upon what he does, or how much he has. The worth of a person, or a thing, or an idea, is in being, not in doing, not in having."

- Alice Mary Hilton

Update

It's September 2007. 18 months since I finished the Diary. I have kept off the weight I lost in that 6 months with some variation around holiday time! My path and direction is clear.

From a very early age, I have always wanted to be a teacher – I have fulfilled this dream and continue in the direction of helping and serving others. Since completing this diary, I have visited Robben Island, South Africa and heard, first hand, from an ex-prisoner, what it was like for Nelson Mandella. I also visited Phi

Phi island in Thailand where 2,300 lives were lost in the Tsunami. I have witnessed extremes of poverty and discrimination. There is much to do in this world and if we all did a little then what a difference we could make.

Who knows where my quest will take me? I am excited about what lays ahead and I continue to be drawn towards individuals and organisations who want to realise their full potential.

Thank you for sharing a little of my world and I hope in some way that my ramblings give you the right sort of nourishment to sustain you on your journey.

9. Further publications
by Mike Wash

Further Publications by Mike Wash:

54 Approaches to Brickwall Management – Managing Change at Work

Have you ever wondered why it is so hard to get people to buy in to what seems to be a sensible, or even brilliant, new idea or way of doing things?

Have you ever felt a little uneasy or unsettled when asked to do something new or change something you have been doing for years?

Have you ever wondered why people react in many sometimes strange, and obstructive, ways to events at work – that should be seen as work?

Have you ever had self doubt about presenting something that maybe new or challenging to your audience?

In this book, I have tried to illustrate the varied approaches (sometime not effective) that people adopt to get others to do things they may initially resist. These approaches also challenge the reader to look at themselves and their own willingness to be open to change.

The situations cover many work related (some would say life related) incidents, eg; redundancy, stress, imposed new systems, change of job, bullying, promotion and many more.

In addition to these are exercises to give you feedback on your effectiveness in managing your personal development, time management, meeting effectiveness and how you work as a team. A questionnaire on leadership will help you gain insight into your own style of influencing others.

Every manager and supervisor should read this book and if your organisation has courage, and wants to create a healthy, thriving work environment, then pass the book on to your staff and ask them to choose an approach which they would like to discuss!!

Good luck in dismantling your brickwalls!

54 Tools and Techniques for Business Excellence

- A book of great value to anyone interested in improving their personal, team or organisational business performance.
- Simple and practical use with handy hints and tips for success.
- Exercises and questions to use with your colleagues.
- Techniques tried, tested and used in the World's best companies.
- From the simplest 'generation of ideas' to transforming total organisation culture.

DESCRIPTION:
- The 54 techniques have been used successfully in all types of businesses and organisations.
- From Health Service to Airline Industry to Manufacturing.
- They form a comprehensive range of techniques for any organisation which is committed to continuous improvement.
- These are the essential basics – the 'must do' and the 'must know' of management and business excellence.

WHO IS THE BOOK FOR?
- Aimed at all managers and staff involved in improvement activities, project management, team work or problem solving.
- Valuable aid to trainers and coaches.
- Great insight for business students who wish to see theory in action.
- Essential for facilitators.

54 Simple Truths with Brutal Advice – How to face the Challenges of Life

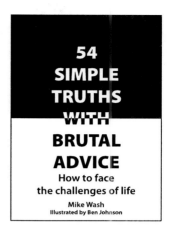

Life is very short and some people go through life never learning or realising that experiences coming their way are inevitable.

The simple truths described here are those inevitable events, incidents and moments that will touch everyone eventually in their life time.

We can make the most of the time we have by being alert and aware of the choices we make in life and the impact they have on ourselves and others. Exploring, debating and reflecting on these simple truths may raise complexities and 'grey' areas, and you may say that there is no such thing as a simple truth.

What may be a truth for some may not be for others. What is simple to some is complex to others. The point here is – it's your choice. You choose what value you gain from these reflective and challenging statements. Challenging; because the truths are accompanied by 'brutal advice'. Brutal only in the sense that there is no complex, theoretical or academic reasoning behind what I write within the book.

I have tried to express the ideas from the heart with good intention that when you pause and ask yourself "so what?" the answer is in the realm of common sense, or direct challenge to some, may come over as a little brutal!

By the way, a word of warning; always be wary of advice given to you. Always better to take your own council, your own choices and your own direction.

Reader Review:

"54 Simple Truths with Brutal Advice" is a common sense guide that provides the reader with a direct no-nonsense approach to living a happy and healthy life at home and at work – two common aspects of life often taken for granted as not being connected.

With topics like life and death, love and loss, risk and reward, author Mike Wash explains the importance of maintaining an earnest sense of responsibility and gratitude when considering the choices and surprises presented to us in life, whether we're dealing with injustice, addiction or success – just to name a few of the many possibilities taken under examination in this work.

Overall the contribution is one designed to participate in a broad field of inquiry as well as to educate and motivate the individual who may be asking similar questions."

This publication is available to order at www.mwauk.com

10. About Mike Wash

About Mike Wash

At the age of 15, after spending 18 months in Catholic School training for a life of a religious teacher as a 'De La Salle' brother, I decided to come home and face the realities of a different type of 'family' life.

The desire within me to help others was still strong and on the eve of me leaving to do Voluntary Services overseas, at the age of 17, an opportunity to join the school of psychiatry as a student nurse was too much of a coincidence to ignore.

Those first few years working in a large mental institution in the early 1970's, wiped out any sense of remaining naivety or innocence about the capability of the human mind to destroy itself and others.

My path was set, but I was unhappy to be constrained by 'institutional walls', so after psychiatry, I trained as a general nurse, then as a tutor – and in my private practice, qualified as a counsellor and psychotherapist.

The constraining nature of the 'health' profession was still too much, so I decided to explore outside, and my horizon changed significantly when I was offered a job in a large telecommunications company. Here, I introduced counselling and the value of developing a supportive, facilitative change management style of leadership.

My premise was that large organisations damage your health – and it doesn't have to be that way.

The irony was that during this time, I battled for 6 months against cancer, which created a greater strength and determination to carry on the path of 'healing', whether in the context of work or family life.

During these very formative years, I also experienced the tragic death of my mother. Following an accident, she was left in a coma for several years. Also, my little sister, who was on kidney dialysis for years before succumbing to hepatitis and kidney failure. I was married young and one of the most proud moments of my life was witnessing the birth of my twin sons.

The strain of tragedy, illness and personal change was too much for my marriage, and divorce eventually cut the chains – which enabled us both to be free and to find new happiness.

I have been running my own business since 1989 and feel very privileged to work with people and organisations passionate about wanting to change and discover their true potential.

I am very happy, married to Mave and enjoying my Grandfather status, and the attention of my sons and step-children. The journey continues ...

11. Index

INDEX